AGING IN ARIZONA: INSIGHTS FOR THE ELDERLY & THEIR FAMILIES

AGING IN ARIZONA
Insights for the Elderly & Their Families

Presley Reader, Mark Young & Steve Alfonsi
with Contributors, Cynthia Findley, Scott M.
Fischer, Marc Giannone, Rhea Go-Coloma, Kevin
Haselhorst, Timothy Holt, Dana Jean, Michelle
Jewell, Andy Lockridge, Jason May, Edward
Perrin, Mindy Wakefield

JONES MEDIA
PUBLISHING

Jones Media Publishing
10645 N. Tatum Blvd. Ste. 200-166
Phoenix, AZ 85028
www.JonesMediaPublishing.com

Printed in the United States of America by Author2Market

ISBN-13: 978-1-945849-44-2

DISCLAIMERS:

This Better Aging in Arizona Guide is for educational purposes only and is not intended to diagnose, treat, cure, or prevent any disease or condition. Please seek qualified professional help for all your social, psychological, and medical needs. In addition, the views and opinions expressed in this presentation are those of the individual authors and do not necessarily represent those of the editors of this Guide, their individual companies, and ComForCare Health Care Holdings, LLC.

The stylized logo COMFORCARE HOME CARE CFC is the exclusive property of Comforcare Health Care Holdings, LLC and used with permission. Other trademarks, service marks, logos, and copyrighted works appearing in this publication are the exclusive property of Comforcare Health Care Holdings, LLC or of the party that provided or licensed the trademarks, services marks, logos, and copyrighted works. For personal use only. All rights reserved. ANY UNAUTHORIZED USE OR REPRODUCTION OF THESE MATERIALS IS STRICTLY PROHIBITED.

INTRODUCTION

Better Aging in AZ

You are getting older; we all are. You have family members who are getting older; we all do. You are experiencing the challenges that come with aging; we all will. But are you proactively managing the aging journey or letting it manage you? Are any of us?

Maybe you are one of the 46.2 million Americans over age 65 who is starting to need support. Maybe you're also one of 65 million Americans providing an average of 20 hours per week of care for a chronically ill, disabled, or elderly family member. You might be a care recipient who doesn't want her children devoting all their time to her and is looking for options. Like so many other older adults you may be experiencing chronic loneliness.

On our weekly radio show, "Aging in Arizona," we often talk about "soapboxes" or touchpoints on the road to getting older. Our main point is that proactivity – planning for the journey – is the most important step you can take to better aging.

Whether you're a caregiver or a care recipient or somewhere in between, this book is for you. It is not a textbook on aging, but, we hope, a useful resource to help you understand the KEY challenges you and your loved ones are likely to face (if you're not already) as you grow older. Understanding and preparing for these challenges is the most important step you can take to **increase your chances** of a positive aging journey.

In the following chapters, our contributors will take you on a road that will arm you with the basics of aging gracefully and smartly. You'll hear from professionals and educators in our community about senior housing options and medication management techniques, smart financial and estate planning, how Medicare and Arizona's Medicaid program work, and finding the right doctor.

Experts will lead you through the realities of caregiving, advance directives, end-of-life planning, and hospice.

This book was inspired by all the wonderful aging experts who have appeared on "Aging in Arizona" (960 AM). When we were approaching our 200th episode, we realized many the same themes were recurring – and so we decided to bring together the expertise under one roof, so to speak, in a book that addresses financial, social, medical and spiritual needs and challenges of getting older. Most the authors of the book have been on the radio show. You will see, as we did, the passion they have for the people they help and the industries they are helping to move forward.

Our ultimate goal is to reduce the stress of caregiving and help you capitalize on opportunities to manage what could be the best years of your life!

Warmly,

Presley Reader, Mark Young
& Steve Alfonsi

A few months ago, Ezekiel Emanuel had an essay in The Atlantic, saying that, all things considered, he'd prefer to die around age 75. He argued that he'd rather clock out with all his powers intact than endure a sad, feeble decline. *The problem is that, if Zeke dies at 75, he'll likely be missing his happiest years.* When researchers ask people to assess their own well-being, people in their 20s rate themselves highly. Then there's a decline as people get sadder in middle age, bottoming out around age 50. *But then happiness levels shoot up, so that old people are happier than young people. The people who rate themselves most highly are those ages 82 to 85.*

– "Why Elders Smile", by David Brooks (NYT 12/4/14)

CONTENTS

Arizona is among the top states in the U.S. with the highest percentage of people over age 65.

Studies have shown that a family caregiver's health is an influential factor in the decision to place an impaired relative in a long-term-care facility.

Caregivers are likelier to lack health insurance due to time out of the workforce.

In 2015, one in five Arizonans was 60 years of age or older, an increase of more than 48% since 2000.

The typical caregiver is a 49-year-old woman caring for a 69-year-old female relative, most likely her mother.

In Arizona in 2015, more than 804,000 people provided 749 million hourse of unpaid care. The dollar value of these hours is more than $9.4 billion. And nationally, the numbers exceed 43.5 million caregivers providing unpaid care valued at more than $470 billion.

The number of Arizonans 85 and older is projected to rise 157% between 2010 and 2030.

A third of caregivers have a full-time job; a quarter work part time. On average, they spend over 24 hours helping care recipients with bathing, dressing, housework, and managing finances.

One in 10 caregivers is 75 years or older.

1

Are You A Caregiver?

**By Cindy Findley, MBA, executive director of
Arizona Caregiver Coalition**

Patti is comfortable calling herself a wife, mother and grandmother. She's also been her husband Hal's sole caregiver for a decade – he has Parkinson's disease. Yet, she thinks of herself as a dutiful wife rather than a caregiver.

> One in three caregivers provides direct financial support to a relative or friend.

Although many people like Patti are spending most of their time in a caregiving role, seldom is the title a welcome addition to one's resume.

Why? Because caregiving can take a serious toll on one's time, health, and bank account. Patti has neglected her own health (she has put off a knee replacement surgery), and she rarely leaves the house. Depression and sleep deprivation have caused Patti to gain weight—making lifting and bathing her husband nearly impossible.

"I am always tired. I can't think straight," she says.

Recognize yourself or someone you know?

> Nearly four in 10 family caregivers of adults report experiencing a moderate to high degree of financial strain as a result of providing care. There is also evidence that family caregiving for parents or a spouse increases the likelihood of falling into poverty over time.

The fact is, there are millions of unpaid caregivers like Patti, people who willingly or unwillingly become the stewards of someone else's care.

And while caregiving has its emotional rewards, research shows there are physical, emotional and economic repercussions that are only going to intensify as the population grays. Caregivers experience depression at higher rates and the chronic stress many are under puts them at greater risk for hypertension and heart disease. Like Patti, many let their own health take a back seat.

> Family caregivers ages 50 and older who leave the workforce to care for a parent lose $300,000, on average, in lost income and benefits over a lifetime.

Studies have shown that an influential factor in a caregiver's decision to place an impaired relative in a long-term-care facility is the family caregiver's own physical health.

The self-care needs are that much more critical because if you can't take care of yourself, how can you be an effective caregiver for others?

Take Care of Yourself

The Family Caregiver Alliance offers these tips for caregivers so they can avoid burnout; an unfortunate side effect of the job:

o   Learn and use stress-reduction techniques such as meditation, prayer, yoga, or Tai Chi.
o   Attend to your own healthcare needs.
o   Get proper rest and nutrition.

- ° Exercise regularly, if only for 10 minutes at a time.
- ° Take time off (respite) without feeling guilty.
- ° Participate in pleasant, nurturing activities, such as reading a good book or taking a warm bath.
- ° Seek and accept the support of others (join a support group).
- ° Seek supportive counseling when you need it, or talk to a trusted counselor, friend, or clergy person.
- ° Identify and acknowledge feelings.
- ° Change the negative ways you view situations.
- ° Set goals.

The Arizona Caregiver Coalition (ACC) can offer help to caregivers. We provide information about resources for caregivers statewide and advocate on behalf of caregivers.

With the help of a federal grant the ACC administers the Respite Rebate Program to give caregivers a much-needed break. Caregivers can apply for reimbursement up to $300 every three months for respite care services for themselves and their loved ones, regardless of medical diagnosis, geographic location, or income. Studies show that the health of the caregiver has a direct correlation on the health of the care recipient. The goal is to keep loved ones out of long-term care facilities and at home. If we can keep caregivers healthy, we can impact the health of care recipients – saving the state $9 billion a year in health care costs.

Future Challenges

The demand for caregivers will jump with the dramatic increase in both the number of older adults and because the fastest growing cohort in that group is people ages 80 and older --the age when people are most likely to have a significant physical or cognitive impairment or both. At the same time, the size of American families is shrinking and the makeup of families is changing as more people do not have children, never marry, divorce, or blend families through remarriage.

Chances are, you are a caregiver or will become one.

Personal experience with community agencies, round-the-clock care, and financial hardships mean you or someone you know understands what the important issues are. This puts family caregivers in a unique position to act as advocates. Get involved and get vocal, locally and nationally, to make caregiver support a critical political, social and economic issue.

SOURCES:

National Alliance for Caregiving and AARP Public Policy Institute.
National Academy of Sciences.
Area Agency on Aging.
AARP.
U.S. Census Bureau.
Family Caregiver Alliance.
National Academy of Sciences.
MetLife Mature Market Institute.
The Commonwealth Fund.
Alzheimer's Association.
Center on an Aging Society.
National Alliance for Caregiving.

Journal of the American Medical Association Internal Medicine.

Journal of General Internal Medicine.

Health Affairs.

Canadian Medical Association Journal.

Annals of Long-term Care: Clinical Care and Aging.

Psychology and Aging.

Journal of Marriage and Family.

Annals of Behavioral Medicine.

New England Journal of Medicine.

The Gerontologist.

Journal of Public Health.

Journals of Gerontology Series A: Biological Sciences and Medical Sciences.

Journal of Psychosomatic Research.

Business Journal.

The Journal of Economics of Ageing.

2

Navigating The Care Of A Person With Dementia: Strategies

By Mindy Wakefield, MSW, Strategic Collaboration Manager, Desert Southwest Chapter Alzheimer's Association

Jane received the devastating diagnosis of Alzheimer's disease four years ago.

Although both she and her husband Tom suspected something was wrong, neither was prepared to hear this. Married almost 30 years, Tom was determined to care for his wife throughout the disease process. Tom did not have children, while Jane had two daughters from a previous marriage living out of state.

As the disease progressed, Jane began displaying behavior not typical of her. She became angry and argumentative toward Tom. She accused her husband of stealing and cheating on her. He tried in vain to convince his wife that these things were untrue. Jane usually responded with increased anger and more accusations. Over time, Tom began to feel overwhelmed with his wife's emotional changes and care needs. She no longer wanted to take a shower, wash her hair, or change her clothes. She followed Tom around the house and became upset when he talked on the phone.

Tom began to feel despair, anger, sadness, and sometimes resentment. He loved his wife and felt it was his responsibility to care for her, but at times he felt like he was failing. Their small circle of friends had dwindled, as Tom spent all of his time caring for Jane. Out of state and with families of their own, he was uncomfortable asking Jane's daughters for help. Tom felt alone, tired, and fearful of the future for both of them.

While every person with dementia is unique, and caregiver experiences differ, the story of Jane and Tom is not an uncommon one. More than 80% of the help provided to older adults with Alzheimer's disease and related dementia in the United States comes from family, friends, or other unpaid caregivers.

Those caregivers face higher rates of depression, poor physical health and economic instability.

In 2016, more than 15 million Americans provided unpaid care for people with Alzheimer's disease and other dementias, according to the Alzheimer's Association.

We'll take you through the stages of caregiving for dementia patients, with tips for keeping your health intact.

Early Stage Caregiving

In the early stages of Alzheimer's most people function independently. They may still drive, take part in social activities, volunteer, and even work. In the early stages, some primary caregivers prefer to use the term "Care Partner" rather than "Caregiver," because a person in the early stages of dementia may not need much assistance.

One of the greatest challenges care partners face is not knowing how much assistance to give or when to give it, because the person with early-stage dementia is primarily independent in dressing, bathing, and walking. The most difficult tasks may involve managing a daily schedule or household budget.

As a care partner, your support with these everyday tasks can help the person with dementia develop new coping strategies that will help maximize his or her independence. Every relationship is different, but finding balance between interdependence and independence may increase confidence for both of you.

To help you determine when and how to provide the most appropriate support, consider these tips:

- Safety First: Is there an immediate safety risk for the person with dementia to perform this task alone? If not, provide encouragement and continue to provide supervision as necessary.
- Avoid Stress: Prioritize tasks or actions that do not cause unnecessary stress for the person with dementia. For example, if you know that grocery shopping will cause frustration for the person with dementia, ask for his/her participation in making the grocery list.
- Make a Positive Assumption: Assume that the person with dementia is capable of completing the task. If you sense frustration, try to identify the cause of the frustration before intervening. Focus on his or her current needs rather than dwelling on the future.

- Create a Help Signal: Identify a cue or phrase that you can use to confirm if the person with dementia is comfortable receiving support. For example, you may agree to use a phrase like, "Is there anything I can do to help?" or a nod to signal that it's okay to chime in if the person with dementia is having difficulty remembering a word or name.
- Talk it Over: The best way to determine how and when to provide support is to ask directly. Ask the person what they need or what frustrations they may be experiencing. Talk about it, then make a plan.
- Work Better Together: Find activities to do together and keep the conversation going about expectations for how you will provide support.
- Check in regularly by asking the person if the assistance you are providing is comfortable or adequate.

Legal and Financial Preparations

The early stages are the time to get legal and financial affairs in order, including powers of attorney, living wills, and advanced directives. A person in the early stages of the disease can participate in this planning and make her own choices. It is often a good idea to consult an elder law attorney to initiate the process or to review legal documents that were completed in a state you no longer live in. Elder law attorneys can also be helpful when applying for Medicaid and/or veterans' benefits.

Middle Stage Caregiving

Communication

As people with Alzheimer's disease gradually lose their ability to find words, express thoughts, and follow conversations, they may also have more trouble understanding others.

Other communication changes during the middle stage include word-finding difficulty, repetition, the invention of new words, the tendency to lose train of thought, difficulty organizing words, reverting to a native language, cursing, speaking less often, and relying on non-verbal communication.

Communicating with a person with Alzheimer's disease should always occur within the context of dignity and respect. Avoid talking down to the person or talking as if he or she isn't there. Try to speak slowly and distinctly, and use a gentle and relaxed tone of voice. Convey an easygoing, non-demanding manner. Be aware of your feelings and attitudes, as they are often communicated through your tone of voice, even when you are not aware of it.

When communicating with a person with dementia, it's especially important to choose your words carefully. Identify yourself and approach the person from the front and at eye level. Make sure to call the person by name and give the person a cue about your relationship. This will help orient the person and get his or her attention.

Some techniques that are often helpful in communicating with a person with Alzheimer's disease include:

- Provide the solution rather than the question. For example, say, "The bathroom is right here," instead of asking, "Do you need to use the bathroom?"

- Avoid confusing expressions. For instance, say, "Please come here, your shower is ready" instead of, "Hop in!" Your family member may interpret it as a literal instruction.
- Avoid vague words. Try saying, "Here is your hat" instead of "Here it is."
- Stress the words in a sentence you feel are most important. Say, "Here is your coffee," instead of, "Here you go."
- Always try to turn negatives into positives. Try saying, "Let's go here," instead of saying, "Don't go there."
- To help demonstrate a task, point to or touch the item you want the person to use. Or, begin the task for the person.
- Avoid quizzing or making the person feel like he or she should know something. Provide cues in your communications. Say, "It will be fun when we visit Susan this weekend," rather than, "Aren't you looking forward to our plans this weekend?"

Behaviors

There are a number of behavior changes that can arise during the middle stage of Alzheimer's disease which can present significant challenges for caregivers. There is frustration because of communication challenges. There may be aggression and agitation. In the middle stage of the disease, a person might experience hallucinations or delusions.

People with Alzheimer's can act in different and unpredictable ways that may be disturbing to you and others. It is important to remember that the person is not acting this way on purpose. All behavior is communication; it is a way of conveying information.

Part of the responsibility of the caregiver is to try to identify the cause of the behavior and possible solutions. There are ways to deal with the behavior changes that can reduce the intensity of the behaviors and the impact on families.

Most of the time the person can be soothed and the behavior can be brought under control by addressing these issues. However, instances of extreme agitation or aggression escalating into dangerous situations do exist.

When the person with dementia or those around him or her are at risk for harm, sometimes, 911 will need to be called. When the emergency team arrives, they will assess the situation and determine whether the person should be taken to the hospital for evaluation. The medical team can then evaluate and treat based on the assessment. They might administer medication to try to bring extremely aggressive behavior under control.

Aggression

There are several possible reasons that a person in the middle stages of dementia may be demonstrating agitation or aggression. It is up to the caregivers to assess the situation to see what may be causing the behavior before attempting to intervene.

Hallucinations or Delusions

Hallucinations, delusions, or paranoia are thought disorders and are symptoms of Alzheimer's disease that may begin or escalate in the middle stages. It is important to discover the source of these symptoms before deciding how to intervene.

Suspiciousness

Memory loss and confusion may cause the person with Alzheimer's to perceive things in new or unusual ways. Individuals may become suspicious of those around them, even accusing others of theft, infidelity, or other improper behavior. Sometimes the person may also misinterpret what he or she sees and hears.

Check with Physician:

- Checking in with the physician can allow you to rule out physical and/or medication problems as soon as possible. For example, sudden and drastic behavioral changes may be due to a urinary tract infection or medication side effects, causing delirium. These problems are often treatable but should be attended to right away.

Medications:

- Although some families find medications to be helpful in reducing anxiety related to hallucination, delusions, or paranoia, there is the possibility that these medications may worsen dementia symptoms. Be careful to use medications only as ordered by the physician, and report any negative effects promptly.

Environment:

- The senses sometimes get overloaded by unfamiliar or sudden environmental changes like new furniture, loud noises, unfamiliar faces, or feelings of being lost or insecure. Make changes to her surroundings when necessary, such as providing adequate lighting and nightlights. Explain the source of the noise.

- Responding to general feelings that are behind specific statements. For example, "My father is at work," when the person's father is actually deceased. The memory of the person may be stronger than the memory of his death. Instead of telling the person that his or her father is dead, try saying, "You must miss your father," or "It sounds like you loved your father very much," or "Tell me about your father."

How to Respond

Don't take offense. Listen to what is troubling the person and try to understand that reality. Then be reassuring, and let the person know that you care. Don't argue or try to convince. Allow the individual to express ideas, and acknowledge his or her opinions. Offer a simple answer. Share your thoughts with the individual, but keep it simple. Switch the focus to another activity. You can engage the individual in an activity or ask for help with a chore. Duplicate any lost item. If the person is often searching for a specific item, have several available. For example, if the individual is always looking for his or her wallet, purchase two of the same kind.

Sundowning

A person with Alzheimer's may experience increased confusion, anxiety, agitation, pacing, and disorientation beginning at dusk and continuing throughout the night. These late-day increases in behavioral problems are often called sundowning. Sundowning can disrupt the body's sleep-wake cycle, causing more behavioral problems.

Sleep changes may be due to a variety of factors, including pain, illness or infection, restless legs, sleep apnea and depression, inadequate exercise and spending too much time in bed.

Sundowning may include several factors. Mental and physical exhaustion from a full day of trying to keep up with an unfamiliar or confusing environment may trigger it. So may increased noise and busyness at home, due to people returning home, having multiple conversations, and preparing for dinner. Reduced lighting and increased shadows may cause persons with Alzheimer's to misinterpret what they see, causing them to be more agitated.

Tips:

- Reduce noise and activity levels. Keep in mind that this is the time of day that is often busiest at home or in a facility. People returning home from work or personnel changing shifts can increase noise levels and upset the person with dementia. You might want to try having the person set up in a quiet area, doing something that will occupy him or her prior to this time of day. You may also want to try turning off the TV and putting on some soothing music.
- Be mindful of your own mental and physical exhaustion. If you are feeling stressed by the late afternoon, the person may pick up on that and become agitated or confused.
- Plan for calm evenings. Plan more challenging activities like doctor appointments, trips, and bathing in the morning or early afternoon hours when the person is more alert.
- Identify triggers. Make notes about what happens before sundowning events, and try to identify triggers.

- Plan light dinners. Have a large meal at lunch and keep the evening meal simple.
- Keep the home well-lit in the evening.
- Do not physically restrain. Trying to restrain the person may make agitation worse.
- Channel restlessness. If the person needs to pace back and forth, you might try allowing this to continue under your supervision. Take a walk outdoors if the weather permits or allow for other forms of exercise, as they may reduce restlessness.
- Talk to your physician about the best times of day for taking medication.
- Use pharmaceutical intervention as a last resort. When behavioral interventions and environmental changes do not work, some people with Alzheimer's may need medication for their agitation during the late afternoon and evening hours. This should be discussed with a doctor.

Start by assessing for pain, which can be caused by medical conditions. Once you and the medical team have ruled these out as possible causes of the behavior, you can help by using behavioral interventions, and may consider using psychotropic medications if necessary.

Have an evaluation for depression performed if early-morning awakening is a problem. Antidepressants given at bedtime may help with sleep. It is important that you use these types of medications only with careful medical supervision. In some people with dementia these medications have the opposite effect, making people more agitated or restless.

Get the person up earlier or keep him or her up later until the person becomes tired. Make sure that the bed and bedroom are comfortable and familiar to the person; a favorite blanket, pillow or bed clothes may be helpful. Do not use bedrails, as they may lead to confusion and a feeling of being trapped. If the person tries to climb out of bed, the bedrails can make it more difficult and a fall can occur. Instead, consider lowering the mattress closer to or on the floor.

Maintain a set bedtime and waking routine and avoid daytime napping unless the person seems very fatigued in the evening. An evening routine of a light snack with herbal tea or warm milk can help relax the person and promote sleep. Allow the person to sleep on a sofa or armchair if preferred. The person may enjoy having soft music playing beside the bed as well. Try to minimize noise, confusion, and the number of people around.

Consider allowing the person to be up at night, if this can be accomplished safely and without destroying the caregiver's routine. You may consider making all or a portion of the house safe for the person to wander in alone at night. Ask others to help supervise the person during some parts of the day or night, and consider hiring a companion for overnight coverage.

Wandering

During the middle stages of Alzheimer's, preparing for and preventing wandering becomes a crucial part of care provision. It is estimated that six in ten people with dementia will wander, and once started most people will do so repeatedly. Wandering is a dangerous behavior, as harm, injury, and even death may occur. If not found within 24 hours, up to half of wandering individuals will suffer serious injury or death. Be aware that the person may not only wander by foot, but also by car or other modes of transportation.

Wandering often occurs as a result of physiological, medical, or environmental changes or disruptions. These changes can include medication interactions or side effects, physical discomfort, stress, physiological changes within the brain, dehydration, sensory overload and/or deprivation, feeling lost, disorientation, a need to search for something, or an inability to negotiate unfamiliar surroundings.

Tips to Reduce Wandering:

- Encourage movement and exercise to reduce anxiety, agitation, and restlessness.
- Ensure all basic needs are met (toilet, nutrition, thirst).
- Involve the person in daily activities to provide him or her with a sense of structure, such as folding laundry or preparing dinner.
- Place color-matching cloth over doorknobs to camouflage them.
- Paint the door and trim the same color as the walls to disguise them.
- Put a dark mat in front of the door. This may be interpreted as a hole and serve as a deterrent from approaching the door.
- Install door alarms.
- Redirect pacing or restless behavior.
- Reassure the person if he or she feels lost, abandoned, or disoriented.
- Keep the home safe and secure by installing deadbolt or slide-bolt locks on exterior doors and limiting access to potentially dangerous areas. Care should be taken to only

do this when the person is supervised so that he or she will have a way out in case of an emergency.

Personal Care

People with dementia slowly become less able to take care of themselves. At first, a person may need only prompting or a little help, but eventually caregivers will become responsible for all personal care.

Loss of independence and privacy can be very difficult. Being aware of the reactions, abilities, and fears of the person with dementia's reactions, abilities and fears can help both the person with the disease and the caregiver have a better experience.

Bathing

Bathing is often the most difficult personal care activity that caregivers face. Because it is such an intimate experience, people with dementia may perceive it as unpleasant or intrusive. They may show their discomfort or distress by screaming, crying, resisting, or hitting. Such behavior may occur because the person doesn't remember what bathing is for, or doesn't have the patience to endure such unpleasant parts of the task as lack of modesty, being cold, or experiencing other discomforts.

The following are ways to improve the bathing experience:

Prepare the Bathroom
Gather the supplies for bathing beforehand, like towels, washcloths, shampoo, and soap so that you and the person can focus on bathing. Check the room temperature to make sure it's not too cold.

Make the Bathroom Safe

To prevent falls, install grab bars on the wall and tub edge. Place non-slip mats on floors. Use a tub bench or bath chair that can be adjusted to different heights. Test the temperature in advance to prevent burns. Never leave the person alone in the bathroom.

Help the Person Feel in Control

Involve and coach the person through each step of the process. You may need to experiment to find out if the person prefers baths or showers. Also, consider what time of day seems to be best.

Include the Person in the Process

Be sure the person has a role in the steps of the process. For example, have the person hold a washcloth or shampoo bottle.

Respect the Person's Dignity

Some people may be self-conscious about being naked. Letting the person hold a towel in front of his or her body, in and out of the shower or tub, may help ease anxiety.

Frequency

It may not be necessary for individuals to bathe every day. Sponge baths with a washcloth can be effective between showers or baths.

Be Gentle

The person's skin may be very sensitive. Avoid scrubbing, and pat dry instead of rubbing. You may want to install a hand-held showerhead to make it easier to wash hard to reach areas.

Be Flexible
Washing the person's hair may be the most difficult task. Ask the person to hold a washcloth over their eyes to avoid getting soap in them.

Dressing

Physical appearance contributes to a person's sense of self-esteem. For a person with dementia, choosing and putting on clothes can be frustrating. The person may not remember how to dress, or may be overwhelmed with the choices or the task itself.

Ways to assist in dressing include the following:

Simplify Choices
Too many choices can be overwhelming. Try laying out clothes or offering only two outfit choices. Keeping the closets free of excess clothing can also minimize distractions.

Organize the Process
Lay out clothing in the order that each item should be put on. You may also hand the person one item at a time while giving short, simple instructions such as "put your arms in the sleeves," rather than "get dressed." Don't rush the person. Haste can cause anxiety.

Choose Comfortable and Simple Clothing
Cardigans, shirts, and blouses that button in front are sometimes easier to work than pullover tops. Substitute Velcro® for buttons, snaps, or zippers, which may be too

difficult to handle. Make sure the person has comfortable, non-slip shoes.

Be Flexible
If the individual wants to wear the same outfit repeatedly, consider getting a duplicate of it or have similar options available. It's all right if the person wants to wear several layers of clothing; just make sure he or she doesn't get overheated. When outdoors, be sure the person is dressed for the weather. If the person's outfit is mismatched, try to focus on the fact that he or she was able to get dressed instead.

Eating

Regular, nutritious meals may become a challenge for people with dementia. They may become overwhelmed with too many food choices, forget to eat, or think they have already eaten. If the person with dementia is not having problems with eating, there is no need to make any changes, but if the person has difficulty, consider the following:

Make Mealtimes Calm and Comfortable
Serve meals in quiet surroundings, away from the television and other distractions. Keep the table setting simple, using only the utensils needed for the meal. Avoid placing items on the table that might distract or confuse the person.

Offer One Food at a Time
The person may be unable to decide among foods on his or her plate. Serve only one or two foods at a time. For example, serve mashed potatoes, followed by cooked meat.

Encourage Independence

Make the most of the person's abilities. Allow the person to eat from a bowl instead of a plate, with a spoon instead of a fork, or even with his or her hands, if it's easier.

Be Flexible to Food Preferences

It is possible the person may suddenly develop certain food preferences or reject foods he or she may have liked in the past.

Be Alert for Signs of Choking

The person may have trouble swallowing some foods. Guard against choking by avoiding foods that are difficult to chew thoroughly, like raw carrots.

Toilet Use

Many people with dementia have loss of bladder or bowel control (incontinence). Causes include inability to recognize natural urges, forgetting where the bathroom is, or side effects from medicine. If this occurs, have the doctor rule out medical problems as the cause. Assistance in toilet use may include the following:

Removing Obstacles

Make sure clothing is easy to remove. Clear the path to the bathroom by moving furniture.

Create Visible Reminders

Posting a sign or picture of a toilet on the bathroom door may help the person find it more easily. Using colored rugs on the bathroom floor and colored toilet lids may be helpful.

Offer Reminders

Encourage the person to use the bathroom regularly. Look for signs of agitation, like facial expressions or pacing, that may indicate the need to go.

Monitor Incontinence

Identify when accidents occur, then prepare accordingly. If they happen every two hours, get the person to the bathroom before that time. Reduce fluids in the evening or schedule bathroom visits in the middle of the night. Consider a bedside commode.

Consider Incontinence Products

Rubber sheets or incontinence pads on the person's bed may help. Padded undergarments or adult briefs are another option.

Late-Stage Caregiving

The journey to the late stages of Alzheimer's is a potentially lengthy process that can last from several weeks to several years. As the disease advances, the needs of a person living with Alzheimer's will change and deepen. Ultimately intensive, around-the-clock assistance is usually required.

A person with late-stage Alzheimer's usually deals with the following:

- Has difficulty eating and swallowing
- Needs assistance walking and eventually is unable to walk
- Needs full-time help with personal care
- Is vulnerable to infections, especially pneumonia

- Loses the ability to communicate with words

Since care needs are extensive during the late stages, your loved may need to move into a higher-level care facility. At the end of life, hospice may be the best option (please see chapter 12, The Hospice Embrace).

I hope we have given caregivers more tools to help their charge navigate a progressive disease with grace. See the Resources page for a guide to community resources and other useful information for caregivers.

SOURCE:

The Alzheimer's Association, "Take Care of Yourself; " 2016. "2016 Alzheimer's Disease Facts and Figures;" "Late-Stage Care;" "Personal Care;" "Living with Alzheimer's for Caregivers." "Early Stage Caregiving;" "Late Stage Caregiving;" "Caregiver Stress;" and "Caregiver Depression."

3

Aging In Place: In-Home Care

By Steve Alfonsi, MA, owner/operator
ComForCare, Scottsdale

> **"There is no place like home."**
>
> **Dorothy**

After caring for my mom while she battled pancreatic cancer, I know how physically and emotionally draining caregiving can be. I'm extremely fortunate to have a loving wife and siblings who assisted and supported me along the way. One of my siblings was even able to take an extended leave of absence from work. Even with this support system, however, the demands were overwhelming.

As a family, we knew, based on conversations with my mom, that her preference was to be in the comfort of her home for as long as possible and we worked hard to honor that wish. Unfortunately, at the time we were not aware of the services that were available to help both her and us, and we didn't take advantage of the one service, in-home caregiving, that would have made the biggest difference. Sadly, while my mom appreciated all that we were doing, we ended up spending our last days with her acting as her caregivers rather than sons and daughters.

An AARP Public Policy Institute report found that almost 90% of people over 65 want to live in their home for as long as possible. For many people, it is not only possible but it may be the most safe and sensible choice.

Here are some of the benefits of aging in place:

- It's more affordable than independent and assisted living communities.
- It reduces anxiety and stress because you are in a familiar environment.
- You maintain relationships built over years with neighbors. Relocating can end these important relationships and create a sense of isolation.
- It reduces the risk of illness. Like hospitals, large independent and assisted living communities can harbor lots of germs due to the number of people; getting colds and illnesses becomes much easier.
- It provides flexibility. Many senior living communities have scheduled dining, activity, and transportation, which restricts the freedom to schedule life around your schedule.

Two adult children recently contacted us at ComForCare as they were investigating caregiving options for their mother. They had decided to relocate their mother to an assisted living community but they were afraid to leave her alone due to some physical and cognitive ailments and depression due to the death of their father.

The children wanted to do right by their mom. What they didn't know was how much she really wanted to "age in place" and how she was going to rebound with the assistance of a home care agency and a specific, well-matched caregiver. We helped the family to understand their mom's wishes – and they decided to keep her in her home with a paid caregiver.

Happily, their mom is still living at home and doing well. She is also, with the caregiver's help, doing things she has not done in years. "She is living a second life," the family told me. They feel she has a new lease on life – and they feel secure with her at home.

Who Pays for What?

When people first explore getting care for their loved one, they are often surprised to hear that Medicare does not cover the expense of having a caregiver in the home.

Also surprising to many Arizonans is that the state does not regulate in-home private duty care. This means there is no licensure or regulatory oversight, so there is a wide range in the quality of services that home care businesses like ComForCare offer.

For example, some businesses known as registries or referral services use contracted workers to provide care. Others like ours, known as agencies, hire, train, and insure their caregivers as true employees. Although the prices could be lower with a contracted model, there can be huge risk associated with using these services. Registries and referral services often do not drug test, background check, or skill-test the caregivers.

And, it is up to the contracted caregiver to have liability insurance that would protect the care recipient if a problem occurs. Most contracted caregivers do not have insurance, which puts them and their clients in danger.

Agencies like ComForCare, on the other hand, perform background checks and drug and skill tests – and we carry general liability and workers' compensation insurance. (For more information about the distinctions between these two types of caregiving business models, visit the Arizona In Home Care Association website at www. aznha.org.)

In-Home and Home Health Care: What's the Difference?

Some people are rightfully confused at the distinction between in-home care and home health care. Home health care is a higher level of care that is deemed medically necessary by a physician and is covered for a time by Medicare or Medicaid.

In-home care, on the other hand, is non-medical in nature and focuses on the support of daily activities, such as bathing, grooming, meal preparation, transportation, activities, and hygiene. Below are some additional differences between the two services:

Home healthcare:

- Doctor-prescribed
- Skilled care, such as wound care
- Specialized caregiving in such areas as rehabilitation
- Nurses can administer medications
- Available for a limited number of hours and days following discharge from a healthcare facility.

In-home care

- Caregivers can provide medication reminders
- Aid with activities of daily living (ADL), such as transfers, bathing, grooming,

- Light Housework
- Meal preparation
- Transportation

Along with this confusion, there are misconceptions about in-home care, including:

- A caregiver at home will take away a person's independence.

  Fact: The caregiver is there to assist the person in keeping his/her independence. Good caregivers and agencies train their staff members on techniques to assist rather than completely take over with care unless necessary.

- Home care is only for people who are ill.

  Fact: Many healthy people need just a little assistance to keep their independence.

- All caregivers steal from their clients.

  Fact: Unfortunately, there are some bad caregivers out there. They tend to be unskilled, independent caregivers not hired through a reputable agency. Therefore, it is important when possible to go through an agency that background checks ALL employees and has liability insurance.

- A person has no say about who comes to their house to provide care.

  Fact: Reputable home care agencies will try to match the required skills and personalities to align with the client. If at any point the client is unhappy, the agency should be willing and able to work with you to find a better fit.

Demographics and the Need for Caregivers

Caregiver Support Ratio				
	1990	2010	2030	2050
USA	6.6	7.2	4.1	2.9
Arizona:	6.8	7.0	2.6	1.8

As baby boomers age, the supply of family caregivers is unlikely to keep pace with the demand. While there were seven potential caregivers per elderly person in the '90s, the caregiver ratio is projected to shrink to just four per person by 2030 nationally and 2.6 per person in Arizona. The gap is then expected to widen even more as the ratio continues declining to 2.9 by 2050 nationally and 1.8 in Arizona, when we'll have three times as many people age 80 and older as there are today.

Technology has assisted us with new ways to stay in contact with a loved one and devices that can detect falls before they happen and dispense medication automatically, and much more that makes it easier to age in place. Yet, despite these advances, it continues to be very difficult to be the sole caregiver for a loved one, a position many find themselves in. Like my own family, many feel that providing hands-on care for a loved one is their duty; however, they could potentially be putting their loved one and themselves at risk for depression, anxiety, substance abuse or drug dependence, and physical ailments.

If you are at the point of exploring or needing professional caregiver assistance, do your homework. Here are some action steps I recommend:

1. Get a professional opinion on how much care is needed for you or your loved one. Quite often a home care agency can provide a Registered Nurse assessment.
2. Know the risks associated with hiring an independent caregiver or registry.
   - Typically, they do not carry general liability insurance to protect you if there is an accident. You might also be liable if they were to injure themselves while assisting you or your loved one.
   - It's suggested to do a background and drug test if possible.
   - Inquire whether they are CPR/First Aid-certified.
   - Check references
   - If you are highly dependent on assistance, put a back-up plan in place should your private caregiver be unavailable one day or need vacation.

Since a license is not required in the State of Arizona to provide non-medical assistance, below is a list of helpful questions to ask, as not all agencies are the same. Home care is similar to many things in life, and quite often you get what you pay for.

- Are your agency caregivers employees of the company or contracted workers? Agency employees tend to be insured by the company, which protects you.
- What percentage of employees do you background check and drug test? Some agency only randomly check. Not all agencies test all employees, and contracted workers tend to not be tested at all.
- Does your agency carry general liability insurance on your employees?

- What percentage of your employees are CPR & First Aid-certified?
- Who on the staff does the care oversight? Are they a Registered Nurse?
- Is your agency a member of AZNHA (Arizona Non-Medical Home Care Association or HCAOA (Home Care Association of America)?
- Do you charge more on nights and weekends? (Many companies will advertise "prices as low as", and have greater costs at various days/times.)

It is important to be proactive in finding care for a loved one. That doesn't mean you can't be the one to do the heavy lifting. But there is no need to risk your own health, family life and job, or compromise your relationship with your loved one. Know that there is help out there.

SOURCES:

AgingCare.com: "10 Signs of Caregiver Stress."
Family Caregiver Alliance.
The Commonwealth Fund.
Center on an Aging Society.
Caregiving as a risk factor for mortality: The Caregiver Health Effects Study, *Journal of the American Medical Association.*

4

Assisted Living Communities: How Do You Choose?

By Scott M. Fischer, BSN, president and co-founder of the Professional Association of Senior Referral Specialists and Community & Facilities Chapter; principle, Options for Senior Living

> "Retirement is like a long vacation in Las Vegas. The goal is to enjoy it to the fullest, but not so fully that you run out of money."
>
> **Jonathan Clements**

In 2016, there were nearly 2,000 licensed assisted living facilities in Maricopa County, along with many new senior living projects. More independent, assisted living and memory care centers are planned in the next few years.

Choosing the right option for yourself or a loved one can be daunting given the sheer number and the complex regulations of senior housing.

In general, senior living communities fall into two categories: unlicensed and licensed.

In the unlicensed category are Independent Living Centers. These are designed to offer lifestyle that includes activities and meals and the opportunity to live with other seniors who still want to maintain an active social life – without having to manage their own home any longer. They're kind of like a cruise ship!

However, it's important to understand that there are no staff or paid caregivers available to residents unless they pay for them privately. Each person can choose to employ a private caregiver or not. Independent Living Centers are unregulated by the government.

In the licensed category are assisted living and skilled nursing centers and in Arizona, behavioral health homes for people with chronic mental illness.

Assisted living is typically divided into two subcategories: large assisted living centers, which have 11 or more residents, and residential assisted living homes with 10 or fewer residents. The former tend to be corporate-owned and located in commercial areas, while the smaller centers are often owned privately and are located in neighborhoods.

A type of assisted living center, Memory Care Centers are dedicated to the care of people with Alzheimer's and related dementias. This type of center may exist as a stand-alone building or as a portion of a larger assisted living center.

Assisted living may have different levels of care. In Arizona, we have the Directed Care license, which is very broad and inclusive, and licenses the highest level of care. The other two levels of care are personal and supervisory. It's important to know the level of care provided in the facility you choose and the kind of license it carries.

Typically, but not in all cases, people who are more reclusive or who need a lot of hands- on and high-touch care during the day are better candidates for the residential assisted living homes. Individuals who still enjoy more social engagement and need a bit less hands-on or personal supervision are better candidates for the larger assisted living centers.

The Cost of Assisted Living

Care costs vary greatly for assisted living. It can range from as low as $1800/month to as high as $10,000, for the most expensive assisted living and memory care facilities. It's fair to say an average $3000--$4500 is a most likely scenario to expect. Though traditional long-term care insurance policies often cover or offset these costs, the vast majority of seniors have not invested in these products, and it's much too late to apply for coverage when the loved one is already experiencing health issues or diagnosed with a cognitive impairment.

Arizona's Medicaid program, the Arizona Long Term Care System (ALTCS), is a lifesaver for many families, as it covers the costs of assisted care plus medications, physicians, and a number of other benefits. However, to qualify, the care recipient must have only about $2,000 in his or her bank account, life insurance policy, annuity, etc.

Some families may also receive benefits from Veteran's Aid and Attendance program. This little-known benefit can increase the income of a veteran who served during specific time periods of war. There is a lengthy application process but many do qualify.

Without state, private, or veterans' benefits, however, many families find themselves having to manage a very heavy financial obligation.

Along with the high cost of care, we see families who, in many cases, have not completed adequate life care planning with designation of Powers of Attorney, Living Will with Advance Directives, or Pre-Hospital Orders for Life Sustaining Treatments.

Without these proper legal documents, it becomes difficult for the family, particularly when trying to make decisions for their loved one who is impaired and who may be considered legally incapacitated.

For example, assisted living in Arizona requires that a Residency Agreement be executed between the resident and/or financial power of attorney and the assisted living facility. When the resident refuses or is unable to sign the agreement, the financial power of attorney may sign and make the contract legal. Without the appropriate forms in place, the family is often forced to pursue legal guardianship and conservatorship, a lengthy, costly, and uncertain process.

Choosing the Right Place

Over the past 20-25 years, an industry of senior referral specialists who place seniors in facilities has emerged. These specialists receive referral fees from facilities, so the family, in essence, pays nothing for the guidance they receive from the agent. This new industry is unlicensed and unregulated, so there can be many issues of performance and integrity in the system.

In order to provide consumer protection and oversight to this industry in Maricopa County, the Professional Association of Senior Referral Specialists (PASRS) was founded by myself and a group of committed agents a non-profit trade association to establish and promote best practices for the agents who engage in this business and for the community at large. For more information about this organization and its participating members, visit www.pasrs.org.

Recently, I was introduced to a man in his mid 60's who was in a skilled nursing facility. He was completing rehabilitation treatment for severe second and third degree burns. This gentleman suffered for many years from mental illness and that had led him to years of isolation from his family. In fact, his only sister had been living out of the country, but they had reconnected and she had come to Phoenix for an extended visit.

During the visit, this gentleman's sister began talking with him about her returning to her home out of the country, and he became upset. He impulsively left home in the late summer afternoon when the temperature outside exceeded 110 degrees. He became dehydrated and lost consciousness. Due to exposure and the extreme temperatures of the asphalt in Phoenix at that time of the year, he was burned severely when he was later found and taken to the hospital for treatment of the dehydration and his burns.

He was later sent to a skilled nursing facility, where he was introduced to me. His behavior had become isolative and concerning to the nursing staff and to the sister, who feared that her brother was not safe to live at home any longer, due to his memory loss and impaired judgment. In many circumstances, this gentleman would likely have been placed in a traditional assisted living home or center, and mixed in with older adults who also suffered with some mild memory loss and cognitive impairment. My wife Stacey and I, however, offered an alternative discharge plan that aligned more with his age and his long history of mental illness.

In Arizona, not only do we have assisted living homes and centers, but, as noted above, we have a selection of licensed behavioral health homes that serve the chronically and severely mentally ill. They assist with activities of daily living, social activities, off- campus opportunities, and the age groups at these homes is more likely to be in the 40-70 years old range rather than the 75-90 years old groups that we often see in more predominantly older adult settings.

Stacey spent hours with the sister and the gentleman to gain his trust and to show her the difference in the settings. His reclusiveness and suspiciousness was really best suited for a licensed behavioral home rather than assisted living. Eventually, he allowed Stacey and his sister to take him to the facility, where he began a new life. He now has housemates, and he assists the manager with some of the household responsibilities, including helping her with the grocery shopping for the home.

Assisted Living: Insurance, Wills, Guardians, Doctors

This story is meant to illustrate some of the important steps to take when considering placing a loved one in assisted living. For example, it's important to have a relationship with a trusted primary care physician. In particular, if there is a long-term care policy that will be activated to be used to pay for or offset the expense of the assisted living, the primary care physician will most often have to complete a certification report that there is need for assisted living services.

Some long-term care insurance (LTC) policies also require a cognitive impairment diagnosis to get the policy to start paying. In this case, the family may need to take their loved one to a neurologist who specializes in memory loss and cognitive impairments. All assisted living facilities will also have admission orders that need to be signed by the primary care doctor, and that can be troublesome to get from the primary care physician when he or she hasn't seen the person in some time. Having a connection to a primary care physician prior to moving into assisted living is important.

As I mentioned earlier, it is also important that Powers of Attorney and Advance Directives be complete.

Arizona also requires a separate and specific document called the Durable Mental Health Power of Attorney. This is necessary when a person requires hospitalization in a behavioral health hospital and he or she cannot or will not sign himself or herself into the facility for treatment. When this document is not available, someone close to the affected person would have to pursue guardianship in order to have the legal authority to hospitalize a person without his or her consent. This process is enormously expensive and can often divide families when it is contested.

A full evaluation of finances is key in preparing for assisted living. If LTC insurance had been purchased, it will be part of the planning process. If a financial planner is involved, I recommend a meeting to lay out a plan of expected expenses against the assets and income available for the senior needing placement.

There are different investment strategies and more financial products introduced all the time to assist families in maximizing their financial resources. This full evaluation will also reveal if it would be necessary to pursue any available public benefits.

Lastly, I recommend you build a team of advisors, including a senior living specialist. We always encourage families to meet with us before they are in crisis. When the previous issues are attended to, it makes planning for and selecting the right assisted living placement so much easier.

Restoring Balance and Health

The greatest joy we see is when a spouse or adult children who have been pouring their lives into caring for a loved one return to their primary role of spouse or child when care is arranged outside of the home in an assisted living home or center. They can sleep better because the care staff at the assisted living facility is there to meet their loved one's needs at night. They tell us that they can now engage and enjoy time with their loved one again without the burden of managing all the details of their life. They tell us that their own health issues – high blood pressure, chronic pain, sleep disorders, and many other things improve.

Although moving is a difficult decision, families often feel they've given their loved one a new, healthier life and that they've also received a new, healthier life.

SOURCES:

The Professional Association of Senior Referral Specialists.
Options for Senior Living.
Arizona Department of Health Services.
Arizona Attorney General's Office.

5

MANAGING YOUR MEDS

By Dana Jean, MBA, Senior One Source

It is no surprise that as we age, we are more likely to develop chronic medical conditions. Outwardly, our metabolism shows itself in changes to our physical appearance and, though not seen, affects the body internally, as well. Our body fat and water composition change as we age, resulting in increased fat storage and decreased water volume.

The way our bodies process medicines changes, too. Medicines (chemicals) metabolize at different rates in the body, especially in the liver. They take longer to leave the body, causing a buildup of chemicals that impacts us in other ways.

Getting older often means seeing more doctors, who manage health conditions with prescription drugs. You may be taking multiple medications, a term called "polypharmacy." Dr.Roy Beveridge, Chief Medical Officer for Humana shared that "IMS Institute for Healthcare Informatics found that people aged 65-79 receive more than 27 prescriptions for new drugs per year" (Many Senior Citizens

Take Too Many Medicines -- Here's How To Fix It). 27 prescriptions in one year!

For healthy and fully capable adults, keeping track of medication dosages and schedules can be challenging. Managing medications can be even more challenging for older patients who are newly diagnosed, managing multiple diseases for several years, in pain, or experiencing dementia.

Several years ago at an American Academy of Family Physicians Scientific Assembly, Aubrey Knight, MD, FAAFP, remarked that "any symptom in an elderly patient should be considered a drug side effect until proved otherwise. A medication is a poison with a desirable side effect." She advised that physicians "consider medication as a possible problem, and not just as the solution" when prescribing medications for elderly patients with multiple chronic conditions.

Following is a summary of the key medication management challenges facing the elderly and their families:

- There are dozens, even hundreds, of medications that are used to treat just one chronic disease, symptoms of the disease, and even treat symptoms of symptoms of the disease.
- Over-medication and drug interaction issues occur frequently. Older adults account for about 35% of all hospital stays but more than half of the visits are marred by drug-related complications, according the U.S. Department of Health and Human Services. Such complications add about three days to the average stay.
- As people age, bodies may not respond to medications the same as when they were young.

- Regular doctor visits are essential to staying healthy and maintaining continuity of care, but staying consisten may be challenging: Transportation can be an obstacle for older adults, especially if the patient is no longer able to safely drive or maintain a vehicle. For those without this support, public transportation and taxi services are an added financial strain.

- Doctor visits often expose the elderly to other diseases and illnesses, especially during cold and flu season. Multiple specialists, in addition to primary care visits, present multiple exposures and risk. It is especially common for patients in the hospital to be admitted and end up with additional illnesses or complications during their stay.

- Elderly people are sent home from the hospital with medication lists that may be very different than when they admitted. Confusion, lack of understanding, poor vision, and stress of change can result in a patient not managing his medications properly, including over-medicating and under-medicating.

- Prescriptions sometimes have side effects that are not pleasant, and can be expensive. Elderly on fixed incomes may decide to lower dosages, stop taking certain medications, and not refill prescriptions to reduce side effects or save money without consulting their medical provider.

- Multiple doctors have different goals for each patient and often do not communicate with one another consistently in most cases.

- Filling new drug prescriptions and disposing of unused or old prescriptions is very confusing, especially for elderly who do not have assistance.

The challenges outlined above are far too common, and are likely familiar to you and your family. Nevertheless, there is hope. With the right information and the right team of family members, friends, and professionals, these medication challenges can be avoided and, in many cases, turned into opportunities.

Some examples:

We were contacted about an older man with high blood pressure, diabetes and gout who was in great pain. A mobile doctor from our team was able to come into the home and assess the challenges. He learned that the man was not correctly taking medications, so we stepped in to provide medication and pain management, adjusting dosages and working with other specialists for a strategic care plan. Caregivers in the home worked with us to clarify how and when to take medications, and played a crucial role in his care. In only one week, the patient's family called to express their gratitude for helping their loved one feel better.

A woman who was new to the community was asking the same question continuously and without ceasing. Our mobile providers did a thorough physical assessment, reviewed the patient's history, which included multiple urinary tract infections (UTI), and documented the medications she was taking. When a UTI is present in an elderly patient who has dementia, it can be catastrophic for the health stability and often ends in a hospital admission if not properly treated or managed. Being able to recognize UTI symptoms with medical history resulted in urinalysis and urine culture being ordered and performed right away. This sweet lady was treated with an antibiotic and symptoms were much better within 24-72 hours, potentially saving the patient from a stressful and unnecessary trip to the emergency room and expensive hospital stay.

In conclusion, there are many steps that older adults and their support team can and should take to maintain a high quality of life, implement effective disease management, and keep loved ones as independent as possible for as long as possible.

Here are some tips to make sure you or your loved one is not over/under-medicating:

1. Be proactive about health care and medication management. This is not possible in every situation, as accidents happen. However, making the effort to be proactive can and will help avoid unnecessary additional challenges.

2. Make sure elderly loved ones visit their primary care doctor on a regular basis and keep an updated list of current specialists providing care. Open communication with all caregivers and professionals will be a huge help or hinder to you.

3. Create a medication list that is taken to every doctor appointment. Some choose to use an Excel spreadsheet, or even a notebook will do. Include prescriptions taken, over-the-counter, and even vitamins and supplements. Maintain a current list so if there is an emergency, emergency providers can make informed decisions about safe medication use.

4. Use one pharmacy if possible. Medication management can be complicated. A good pharmacy can add another level of protection when it comes to similar medications and potential interactions. Ask the pharmacist to include what each prescription is treating on every bottle. If you're

concerned about any of them, ask questions. They are there to help!

5. Keep a list of questions for office visits to the doctor. Medical providers cannot read minds. If you do not share concerns, they cannot be addressed. Ongoing conversations about minimizing medications is helpful also.

6. Choose a primary care physician wisely. Your primary care doctor should be the hub for your medical needs. Find a provider who is interested in getting to know you and is willing to be available to communicate with you and with other specialists involved in your care.

7. Select providers who effectively utilize technology. For example, medical information can be shared electronically. This is not available in all offices and healthcare areas, but is becoming the norm. This enables multiple providers and specialists to look at a centralized medical record that can be used in regular visits and emergency situations.

8. Consider a mobile primary care/home health service. In the last fifty years, house call providers have almost disappeared and are more often regarded as old-fashioned. Technology and a rising senior population have resulted in house call companies making a comeback for elderly and homebound patients. Mobile providers help eliminate barriers that vulnerable populations have, including transportation, social, emotional, and financial. These services help prevent the inconvenience of hospitalizations, 911 calls, and trips to the emergency room. House call doctors help with the transition from hospital stays to home following emergency situations, chronic conditions, or surgeries.

9. The American Geriatric Society released a report titled "Beers Criteria for Potentially Inappropriate Medications Use in Older Adults". This report identifies medications that seniors (65+) should avoid or use with caution. This is a fantastic resource, but should be used in conjunction with healthcare professionals.

10. Communicate, communicate, communicate! There are no stupid questions. Ask them.

There are many challenges and opportunities facing the elderly, their families, and our communities. Medications are just one example. Fortunately, there are many professionals who are passionate about their specialty and, even more important, passionate about helping seniors and their families. Being proactive and becoming educated about what is available in the community can determine what kind of care a loved one can experience in his and her later years.

SOURCES:

Has overmedicating seniors become 'America's other drug problem (2016). PBS Newshour. Retrieved from http://www.pbs.org/newshour/rundown/polypharmacy-americas-drug-problem/.

How Many Pills Do Your Elderly Patients Take Each Day? (2010). MD Peer Exchange. Retrieved from http://www.mdmag.com/conference-coverage/aafp_2010/how-many-pills-do-your-elderly-patients-take-each-day.

Many Senior Citizens Take Too Many Medicines -- Here's How To Fix It. (2014). Forbes. Retrieved from https://www.forbes.com/sites/matthewherper/2014/12/10/many-senior-citizens-take-too-many-medicines-here-are-three-fixes/#70a9cb74692d.

Beers Criteria for Potentially Inappropriate Medication Use in Older Adults http://www.americangeriatrics.org/files/documents/beers/BeersCriteriaPublicTranslation.pdf.

6

The A,B,C And D
(And Other Basics) Of Medicare

**By Michelle Jewell, licensed Medicare broker
and educator**

Medicare. The mere word can bring up anxious feelings, confusion, and worry. I am often asked "Why does it have to be so hard?" and I wish I had a magic answer. I can tell you that, if you put in some time and effort, it will become easier to understand. I hope the following information clears up some of your questions and concerns, and helps you age gracefully and healthfully into Medicare.

First, a primer:

Medicare is health insurance for people 65 and older, people under 65 with certain disabilities, and people of any age with end-stage renal disease (ESRD). President Lyndon B. Johnson signed Medicare into law in 1965. Today, more than 55 million Americans are covered by Medicare; by 2050, the number will be 93 million.

Sound simple? Let's move on.

Medicare is broken down into four different groups: Parts A, B, C, and D.

Part A covers the following:

- Hospitalization
- Skilled nursing facility (SNF) care
- Hospice care
- Home health care

Usually you don't pay a premium for Part A coverage. If you or your spouse worked 10 years, or 40 quarters, you are automatically enrolled in Part A when you turn 65. If you did not work the full 10 years or 40 quarters, you may be able to buy Part A and pay a premium. All in all, it covers you while you are in the hospital. In 2017, the yearly deductible for Part A is $1,316.

> **Myth:** Medicare covers all your health insurance costs with no copay or deductible.
>
> **Truth:** When you use a Medicare-covered service for your health care, Medicare typically pays 80% and you pay 20% after you have met your deductible. You can go to any hospital or doctor anywhere in the U.S. that accepts Medicare. There is no annual limit on out-of-pocket costs.

Part B covers the following:

- Doctor visits
- Outpatient care
- Diagnostic and laboratory tests, such as X-rays and blood work
- Durable medical equipment (e.g., diabetic test strips, canes, oxygen)

- Some preventative services (e.g., vaccinations, mammograms, colonoscopies)
- Ambulance services

Monthly premiums for Part B (most recipients pay $134 in 2017) come out of your Social Security check. If you are not taking Social Security you will be billed quarterly. In addition, you will pay an annual deductible ($183 in 2017) before your coverage begins. Single people with incomes higher than $85,000 and married couples filing jointly who have an income over $170,000 pay a higher monthly premium.

Myth: Medicare covers all of your health care needs.

Truth: Medicare does not cover:

- Most dental care
- Eye examinations related to prescriptions
- Dentures
- Cosmetic surgeries
- Hearing aids and exams for fittings
- Long-term care

Part C (Medicare Advantage):

- Includes benefits and services covered under Parts A and B
- Usually includes Medicare prescription drug coverage (Part D) as part of the plan
- Is run by Medicare-approved private insurance companies
- May include extra benefits and services for an extra cost
- Has an annual limit on out-of-pocket costs

To qualify for a Medicare Advantage plan you must live in the plan's service area, be enrolled in both Medicare Part A and B, and you cannot have end-stage renal disease (ESRD). You must also continue to pay your Part B premium in addition to any premiums the plan may charge. Some people believe if they have a Medicare Advantage plan they no longer have Medicare, this is not true.

In many cases plans will offer above and beyond what Medicare offers for benefits, such as some vision, dental or hearing services and use of fitness facilities. Co-pays, benefits, premiums, and costs can vary greatly between the plans. It is important to review your plan every year to be sure you are receiving the best coverage for your needs.

Most Medicare Advantage plans have networks that you must use to receive your services (like doctors, hospitals, or pharmacies). If you use a service outside of the plan's network, there can be additional costs. Most, but not all, Medicare Advantage plans offer coverage for prescription drugs. When finding a plan to fit your needs you will want to check if your doctor(s) is in the plan's network and that your prescription drugs are in the plan's drug formulary (drug list).

A Medicare broker who contracts with most of the Medicare Advantage plans offered in your area can help you sort through the many choices. Brokers are paid by the insurance companies and are paid the same rate regardless of which company you choose. This helps create an unbiased system, so you can be comfortable knowing you are getting the plan that best fits your needs. Keep in mind that there is no guarantee your doctor will stay with the Medicare Advantage plan you choose for the entire year.

There are several types of Medicare Advantage plans:

- Health Maintenance Organizations (HMOs)
- Preferred Provider Organizations (PPOs)
- Private Fee-for-Service plans (PFFS)
- Special Needs Plans (SNPs): For people who have a chronic or disabling condition such as diabetes, COPD or congestive heart failure. SNPs may also be available to people who also receive Medicaid and who live in care facilities like nursing homes.
- Medical Savings Accounts

Medicare Savings Programs

There are additional programs available that help people with Medicare who have limited income and resources. These programs can help pay for Medicare Part A and B costs, such as premiums, deductibles, and copayments. If you have Medicare and full Medicaid coverage, most of your health care will likely be covered. There are different levels of assistance depending on your income and resources. Contact your local or state Medicaid office to see if you qualify and to apply.

Part D (Medicare prescription drug coverage)

- Helps cover the cost of prescription drugs
- Is run by Medicare-approved private insurance companies
- May help lower your prescription drug costs and help protect against higher costs in the future

There are two ways to enroll in Medicare Part D drug coverage: Original Medicare with a stand-alone drug plan, or with a Medicare Advantage plan.

Most Medicare drug plans have their own list of covered drugs, known as a formulary. Each formulary normally has up to five tiers or levels, with the lowest representing the lower-cost medications.

A great resource for finding a drug plan is on the Prescription Drug Plan Finder located at www.Medicare.gov. It can be used to find a plan that suits your medication needs. It is important to understand how drug coverage works:

- Premiums: Monthly costs vary according to the plan you choose and your income.
- Stage 1-Annual deductible: If your plan charges a deductible, it is the amount you pay before your coverage begins (in 2017, up to $400).
- Stage 2-Initial Coverage Period: When the total cost of your drugs for the given year (including what you have paid and what the plan has paid) reaches $3700 (2017), you move into the coverage gap, or "donut hole," which is a temporary limit on what Part D will pay for medication.
- Stage 3-Coverage Gap or "Donut Hole:" For the coverage gap in 2017 you will pay 40% of the cost of brand-name drugs and 51% of the cost of generic drugs. How you move out of the coverage gap is determined by adding together the deductible, coinsurance and copayments, what you have paid in the coverage gap and the discount you received on your covered brand-name drugs while in the coverage gap.

- Stage 4-Catastrophic Coverage: When the total reaches $4950 (in 2017) you will pay no more than 5% of the cost of the drug until the end of the year.

Penalties to Avoid

If you purchase your prescriptions at an "out-of-network" pharmacy, chances are you will pay more for your drugs and you may end up in the coverage gap sooner than expected. Also, do not delay in enrolling in a Part D drug plan. If you miss your Initial Enrollment Period when you are first eligible, you may pay a penalty that will stay with you for the rest of your life.

If you have "creditable" drug coverage through an employer you may not need to sign up for Part D when you turn 65. If you lose the coverage, you'll have 63 days to enroll without a penalty.

Help paying for Part D drug costs

If you have limited income and resources, you may qualify for Extra Help paying for your prescription drug costs. Extra Help is a Medicare program designed to help people pay their Medicare prescription drug costs. There are income and resource limits to qualify. For more information or to apply, call Social Security at 1-800-772-1213 or visit them online at www.socialsecurity.gov/Medicare.

Enrollment in Medicare

As you approach your 65th birthday, you will automatically be enrolled in Medicare Part A and Medicare Part B if you are already receiving your Social Security benefits or Railroad Retirement Benefits (RRB). Your Medicare card and a "Welcome to Medicare" kit will automatically come to you in the mail approximately three months before your birthday. If you are not receiving your Social Security or RRB, you must apply for Medicare Part B. If you don't apply, you will not be enrolled and will more than likely pay a hefty penalty down the road.

Initial Enrollment Period (IEP)

You can sign up for Medicare Part A or Part B during a seven-month window that includes the three months before your 65th birthday, the month of, and three months after. This is when the majority of people sign up for Medicare, to avoid a penalty. Your coverage normally begins the first day of the month of your 65th birthday, unless your birthday is the first of the month. Then it will begin the first day of the previous month. If you signed up in the three months after your birthday month, your coverage will begin the first day of the following month.

If you miss the Initial Enrollment Period, you have another chance to enroll during a General Enrollment Period (Jan. 1-March 31), but you may face a penalty depending on your reason for missing the IEP.

- You will incur late penalties equaling 10% that are permanently added to your Part B premiums for each 12-month period you delayed enrollment. For example, if you delayed your enrollment for three full years, your premiums can be 30% more!
- You will have late penalties permanently added to your Part D premiums for each month that you did not have "creditable" drug coverage since turning 65. Creditable coverage means coverage from another source that Medicare considers as good as Part D coverage. If you

qualify for Extra Help for Part D you many not pay late penalties.

Open Enrollment Period is from October 15th to December 7th each year, with coverage starting January 1st. This is when you can change your Medicare Advantage plan or prescription drug coverage for the following year.

Special Enrollment Period (SEP)

You can enroll in Medicare without penalty during a Special Enrollment Period (SEP). You qualify if:

- Loss of qualifying health care coverage through your job
- Moved to a new area or state
- You joined a Medicare Advantage plan when you were first eligible for Medicare, and within the first 12 months you decided to switch back to original Medicare

In many cases, the Medicare plan you sign with will need proof that you are entitled to a Special Enrollment Period.

Note: COBRA coverage and retiree health plans aren't considered creditable coverage. You will not be entitled to a Special Enrollment Period when it ends. To avoid penalties, make sure you sign up for Medicare when you are first eligible.

Medicare Supplemental Insurance or Medigap

Another choice for health insurance in addition to Part A and B is a Medicare Supplement policy, often known as Medigap. If you enroll in a Medigap policy, Medicare pays its share of the Medicare-approved amount and the Medigap policy pays its share. You pay a monthly premium to the insurance company. Every Medigap policy is governed by federal and state laws and all policies offer the same basic benefits. The plans are labeled A-N with varying coverages and costs. The plans are through private insurance companies and they can choose which of those plans to offer.

Medigap policies offer nationwide coverage and, in many cases, worldwide coverage. Many people who are turning 65 or retiring and want to travel choose a Medigap plan. You can generally go to any hospital, any doctor, anywhere in the United States that accepts Medicare. The cost of a Medigap policy can differ greatly from one company to another, while offering the exact same plan. It is important to shop for your coverage carefully.

The best time to enroll in a Medigap policy is during your Medigap Open Enrollment Period. This is a six-month period that begins the first day of the month you turn 65 or are enrolled in Medicare Part B. Medigap policies do not have Part D drug coverage included. You will need to enroll in a Part D Prescription Drug Plan (also known as a PDP) separately and within your Initial Enrollment Period to avoid a penalty

Once you have your plan in place, as long as you pay your premiums you are generally "guaranteed renewable" for as long as you have your policy. This means your health insurance company cannot cancel your policy due to health problems. If you leave the plan voluntarily, it may be difficult to re-enroll at a later date without health questions.

Group health insurance from a current employer

If you or your spouse are still working, and you have health care coverage under an employer plan, contact your employer's HR department to see how coverage works with Medicare. In many cases, you may not have to sign up for Medicare Part B and can delay the cost. Once employment or coverage ends, you have eight months to sign up for Medicare Part B without penalty. It is important to keep the letter of termination from the employer stating the insurance is ending. In many cases, the Medicare plan you sign with will need proof that you are entitled to a Special Enrollment Period. It is important to note that if you are retiring and no longer working but covered under an employer's insurance you will need to sign up for Medicare Part B to avoid penalty.

Medicare and Social Security Disability Insurance (SSDI)

Social Security Disability Insurance gives income to people who are unable to work and are disabled. After you receive SSDI benefits for two years (24 months) you are automatically enrolled in Medicare Part A and B. Your Medicare card will be mailed to you about three months before your 25th month of disability. If you don't receive it, you will want to contact your local Social Security office.

I hope this chapter has helped you to understand the basic workings of Medicare. As you have read, there are many options to consider depending on your circumstances and your needs.

A comprehensive review by a licensed professional is the best way to make a decision on what plan is best for you for the coming year. Choose your plan wisely, and you will have less to worry about and more time for a happy life. I wish you good health and blessings.

SOURCES:

CMS.gov "On its 50th anniversary, more than 55 million Americans covered by Medicare:" July 28, 2015.

U.S. Census Bureau, Population Division, Interim State Population Projections.

Medicare & You 2016, the official U.S. government Medicare handbook.

Statista.com: "Statistics and Facts About Medicare."

7

LONG-TERM CARE: WHAT WILL ARIZONA COVER?

By Jason May, Esq. Gaudiosi Law,
Peoria/Scottsdale

We are living longer, but many of us are not living well. Why? Often, we don't have the social or financial resources to support our needs. I am an estate planning attorney, and when people first meet me their main interests are preventing the government from getting their money, and deciding and describing where their things will go after they are gone.

We will all, indeed, be gone at some point, and planning for that inevitability is wise. However, I teach people that most of our lives are less like a light switch that turns off and more like a dimmer switch, fading as the knob of time is twisted. What is their plan for that period of "dimming," I ask. This is why long term care education and planning is so important, and this is also why every Arizona resident needs to understand Arizona Long Term Care System.

ALTCS is a state-funded service that covers certain skilled nursing/nursing home and in-home services. ALTCS won't pay for assisted living, but it will cover nursing home care, and many states like Arizona cover in-home care services for eligible people. In fact, in-home and community-based services (HCBS) are preferred by the state and members alike. Costs to the state are generally lower, and the quality of life for recipients is higher, as they get to stay in a familiar environment.

ALTCS is not, however, available for everyone. Like most government programs, ALTCS has specific qualification requirements which must be met in order for an individual to receive benefits. In the case of ALTCS, the qualification process includes three components.

1. Medical: You must be assessed by the Arizona Health Care Cost Containment System (AHCCCS), and they must determine that the individual seeking care is in need of nursing home-level care. Once you apply, your condition will be evaluated by a state employee according to their criteria.

2. Financial Part 1 (Income): Your monthly income (including all VA Pension benefits) is limited to 300% of the Federal Benefit Rate (FBR) which, for single persons as of 1/1/15, must not exceed $2,199. This number changes depending if you are married or single, if both or just one spouse is needing ALTCS, and may be modified by changes in the FBR.

3. Financial Part 2 (Assets): A single person cannot have more than $2,000.00 in countable assets. ALTCS does not include the following assets in this calculation: principal residence with equity of $500,000 or less, one vehicle valued at $4,500.00 or less, life insurance with a cash value under $1,500, burial plots, or irrevocable prepaid funeral plans.

Let's look at a fictional scenario to further illustrate the qualification requirements. Linda can no longer live on her own and is in desperate need of long-term care. Unfortunately, even with her pension from the state, Social Security, and spousal benefit, Linda can't afford the level of care she needs. She is only bringing in $2,700 a month. Linda owns her home, which is valued at $220,000, a car that she rarely drives, which is worth $3,500, some household and personal keepsakes, and a prepaid burial plot next to her husband's.

Linda's savings and husband's IRA have sustained her these last few years, but they are quickly dwindling. After reviewing her complete situation, Linda learned most her assets were non-countable, allowing her to meet the $2,000 asset requirement after only a short spend down time. Although Linda's income exceeded the current federal threshold ($2,199/mo), if she used an Income Only Trust, she would meet the limit. After Linda was medically approved, she would have the choice to remain living at home, move in with family, or move into an AHCCCS-certified nursing or assisted living facility.

Here's a real-life example: Esther contacted me because she had some changes she wanted to make in her will and other estate planning documents. While reviewing her situation, I learned Esther was a sharp, independent, 84 years young. She lived on her own in a simple apartment in South Phoenix. Her husband had passed away 15 years prior to our meeting. She had a used car worth $3,000. She lived off $1,800 per month from a pension and Social Security. She had a little spending money monthly from an annuity, but no other savings. Her sons and grandchildren lived within an hour of her, and visited regularly.

As Esther and I spoke, I answered her questions about her intended estate plan changes. But more important, what was her plan if she suddenly could not care for herself? Was she familiar with ALTCS?

She insisted she did not need any assistance because she was doing fine, and she was right!

Based on the qualification requirements we discussed earlier, Esther would not be medically eligible for ALTCS, even though she qualified financially. And, she figured when the time came for medical care, she would be ready to die. Remember the dimmer switch? I told Esther I agreed that she did not need ALTCS right then. In fact, she would not likely qualify as she was likely missing the medical requirement, and I told Esther I was fortunate to meet her when she was physically fine and making ends meet. I reminded her, though, that she was one fall or hospital stay away from being in great trouble, and the best time to plan is when there is not an emergency. We discussed how she could plan if that time ever came. We discussed what needed to be done and what she could take care of now to help make it easier on her family later. When we finished, Esther understood the process. She had the ALTCS Pre-Screening and Application information in hand. Would she do anything with it?

As you can see, there is much misunderstanding about the ALTCS application and approval process. Here are six more myths and facts to consider.

1) I plan on using ALTCS, so I don't need long-term care insurance.

   Fact: Having a qualified policy may save part of or all of your estate from ALTCS-related liens on your estate. Under the Arizona Long Term Care Partnership Program, the Arizona Long Term Care System (ALTCS) does not count some of or all of the applicant's resources (assets) when determining eligibility if the applicant has a long-term care insurance policy that meets certain requirements. (Arizona's Eligibility

Policy Manual for Medical, Nutrition, and Cash Assistance, Chapter 703.11.)

2) I already have Medicare so I don't need ALTCS.
   Fact: Long-term care is not covered under Medicare. ALTCS is specifically designed to address the long-term care issue.

3) The IRS allows for gifting, so I'll just give my property away so I can qualify for ALTCS.
   Fact: ALTCS rules and the federal tax code are very different, and following one does not guarantee adherence to the other. ALTCS gifting may be allowed but only in very limited circumstances. Applicants or prospective applicants should never give away their assets without guidance from an ALTCS specialist.

4) My property is in a living trust so it doesn't count as an ALTCS asset.
   Fact: Property in a living trust is still viewed as the applicant's property under ALTCS. Furthermore, a normally ALTCS-exempt home will lose its exemption when placed in a trust. Make sure that before you put in or remove property from a trust for ALTCS planning you consult with a specialist or Elder Law attorney.

5) My spouse needs long-term care but ALTCS will kick me out of my house if we apply.
   Fact: ALTCS is empowered to recover costs incurred from an ALTCS recipient's estate via liens. However, the healthy spouse may qualify for one of several exemptions, including the family home.

6) My income is higher than the ALTCS allowed amount, so I'll never qualify, but I cannot afford the care I need.

Fact: The federal government allows for an otherwise-ineligible ALTCS applicant based on income to create a special Income Only (or Miller) Trust that allows applicants to qualify for services.

Nine months after I met with Esther, I got a call from her son. She had fallen and injured her hip and shoulder. She was no longer able to live on her own. Thankfully, Esther had completed the ALTCS pre-planning just a few months prior, which put her in position to get the help she needed.

Be Esther. Educate yourself not only about ALTCs, but also the other long-term care challenges. Attend seminars, meet with experts in Medicare, Medicaid/ ALTCS, estate planning, senior living and caregiving options, and talk to your friends. Make a plan which includes your estate (will, trusts, deeds, accounts, personal property), yourself (financial, health care, mental health powers of attorney, living will/advance directive, guardian/conservator nominations, instructions for your remains), your care (staying at home versus an all-inclusive senior community), and your insurance (private health care versus Medicare or long-term care versus Medicaid/ALTCS).

If you have a plan, have it reviewed at least every five years, or when a life event occurs. Things change, the law changes, services change, your family changes and, yes, even you change. Have a plan that meets your needs for today and tomorrow, not yesterday.

SOURCES:

AARP.

Family Caregiver Alliance.

U.S. Department of Health and Human Services.

Arizona Health Care Cost Containment System.

8

PRIMARY CARE:
STAYING HEALTHY AND WHOLE

By Ed Perrin, MD, family physician and geriatrician

Optimizing your health is about following the basics: Keep your vaccines up to date. Don't use tobacco. Get physical by walking, swimming, hiking, bowling – whatever gets you moving. Feed your brain by reading and discussing books and newspapers, learn a new skill or language. Stay socially active by joining a church group or dinner club. Stick to whole foods like vegetables, beans and whole grains.

And if you are fortunate to keep your good health over the long haul, schedule a primary care doctor visit once a year. You may even want to see a primary care doc who is certified in geriatrics - the care of older adults. More on that later.

So what does a primary care doctor do, exactly? Let's contrast it with secondary care, tertiary care and quaternary care:

Secondary care includes the services that subspecialists provide to patients, doctors that include dermatologists, cardiologists, surgeons, etc. Tertiary care is the medical care that is provided in a hospital (or emergency room). Quaternary care is highly-specialized hospital care, like transplants or experimental treatments.

All levels of care listed above are invaluable, and many are life-saving. However, they are episodic; you need them on a case by case basis unless you have a chronic or acute condition.

Your primary care, on the other hand, is there for the long haul. It begins in infancy and continues through your lifetime.

Principles of Primary Care

Primary care rests on four core principles: comprehensive care, coordinated care, access to care, and patient-centered care. The doctor-patient relationship is ideally long-term.

Because primary care doctors offer comprehensive care – everything from simple colds and coughs to managing chronic conditions like heart disease, emphysema, and diabetes – they are the cornerstone of good health.

Studies show that communities with less access to primary care providers are less healthy. For example, communities with more primary care providers see higher rates of seatbelt use, tobacco cessation, physical activity, healthy eating, and immunizations.

Specific health measures that are improved with greater access to primary care include: death rates overall and due to conditions such as heart disease and cancer; rates of low birth weights; hospital admissions; teen pregnancy rates; infant mortality; and life expectancy.

If one additional primary care physician were available for every 10,000 people in any given community, it has been estimated that over 100,000 deaths annually could be prevented in the United States.

Primary Care and Older Adults

Arizona has a shortage of primary care doctors and even fewer geriatricians, primary care doctors who have additional training in caring for vulnerable older adults.

Approximately 150 board-certified geriatricians are licensed to practice medicine in Arizona (I am one of them). Yet the anticipated need for geriatricians for 2015's most vulnerable older residents was 506, putting Arizona near the bottom in its numbers. Moreover, many rural counties in Arizona have even fewer geriatricians, or even none. And many board-certified geriatricians (check certificationmatters. org to get a list) restrict their practice to academic settings, hospice care or institutional care.

Only the most vulnerable older adults truly need the services of a geriatrician. But some may value the insight and perspective such a doctor can provide.

Geriatricians are trained to see the person in the context of his or her family and community. They know which questions to ask. They focus on function rather than just a set of symptoms: how does the patient get through the day? What resources are at their disposal? What is their financial status?

Getting a social history is important to the geriatrician in treating the whole patient. This is not unique to geriatricians; all physicians are trained to obtain social histories, yet geriatricians' social histories typically are deeper, more personal, and focus on salient elements like social support, finances, faith, family members and their associated dynamics.

In addition, the geriatrician has a deeper understanding of "multi-morbidity," the conditions that tend to live together and how they inter-relate, and can apply his or her experience when treating the older person.

Questions to Ask

If a board-certified geriatrician is not readily available to provide primary care (which will more often than not be the case), the most important question you should probably ask is whether a primary care provider offers comprehensive and coordinated care. A little research will give you the answer:

Look at the practice website, call an office manager to discuss your concerns, schedule a tour of the office and perhaps meet briefly with the doctor you are considering.

Other questions to keep in mind when investigating whether a primary care physician is the right fit for an older patient include:

- Are same-day/next-day appointments available?
- Will the doctor, or someone from the office, be involved in the care delivered in a hospital or skilled nursing facility?
- What relationships does the office have with other providers (secondary or sub-specialty care, physical therapy, pharmacies, home health agencies, etc.)?
- Are labs and x-rays available on-site?
- Is a doctor available by phone after hours?
- Is there a patient portal to access the electronic medical records from home?
- Is non-visit-based care available (e-mail, text, video, phone, etc.) and/or home visits available, and if so, are they welcomed, or viewed as an additional burden?

Other Primary Care Concerns

No matter what type of primary care physician older Arizonans choose to see, occasionally a longer visit – more than 15 to 20 minutes -- is preferable.

And no matter the type of primary care physician they see, it should be done at least once annually (or more, of course, for patients with chronic conditions). This visit should focus on conditions that may be silent or hidden, in addition to going over known or established diagnoses and concerns. In addition, preventive tests and interventions should be offered, including vaccinations, cancer screens, and mental health considerations.

The goal of this annual visit is to maintain health, prevent avoidable illness, and catch problems early before they become serious. Although many Arizonans' biggest medical fear is a cancer diagnosis, most authorities recommend only a few cancers to be screened for, and only in average-risk patients who have at least a fair life expectancy. Specifically, we screen for cervical and breast cancer in women, colon cancer in both men and women, and lung cancer in current or former smokers who have quit in the past fifteen years.

When a visit to a doctor is required, it is important for the patient to be prepared for the visit. Preparation includes a knowledge of all medications: prescription and over-the-counter; especially oral, topical, and inhaled ones; their generic and brand names, if they have them.

Also be prepared to share information about conditions you may have and have had.

Finally, and probably most importantly, a complete list, preferably written, of all concerns and questions, should be provided to the doctor at the beginning of the visit.

These steps are valuable when spending time with a primary care physician.

Minimizing Doctor Visits

As we age, our best times should not be sitting in doctors' offices but rather enjoying any other activity: spending time with family, including spouses, children, grandchildren, and parents; socializing, whether it be at a senior center, a recreation center, a city park, or a place of worship; volunteering; or traveling, among countless other pastimes or activities.

This is not to say that older Arizonans and their children should avoid going to doctors' offices, but rather that they should avail themselves of primary care (and consequently all medical care) very judiciously.

For healthy patients, an annual evaluation at their primary care doctor's office is often the best medicine."

9

LOOKING AHEAD: THE WISDOM OF LONG-TERM CARE INSURANCE

By Andy Lockridge, life and health insurance broker

In the next two decades, a combination of demographic changes and budgetary strains will create an explosive – and possibly unsustainable -- demand for long-term care services for seniors.

> "Someone's sitting in the shade today because someone planted a tree a long time ago"
> -Warren Buffett

With the cost of such care ranging from $40,000 to $100,000 per year, personal savings and assets will quickly disappear unless you take steps to protect them.

One vehicle for covering long-term care and protecting your assets is long-term care insurance (LTC), a plan that finances the day-to-day caregiving for people with a chronic illness or loss of cognitive ability or mental capacity.

What does LTC cover?

Most long-term care insurance policies pay for the cost of care in three main areas:

- **Home Health Care:** It is estimated that 75% of people living today will receive home health care at some point during their lifetime. Home health care can include the following areas: part-time skilled nursing care, practical nursing assistance, physical/occupational therapy, homemaker assistance, and assistance with activities of daily living (ADLs). The average cost in the U.S. is around $3,800 per month, according to Genworth's 2016 Cost of Care survey; that cost is expected to rise to $5,100 by 2026.

- **Assisted Living Care:** When a person is no longer able to stay in their home, they often move into an assisted living facility. An assisted living facility often provides room and board and care for a daily or monthly fee. Typically, in order to qualify for care in an assisted living facility, a person must need assistance with at least two activities of daily living (ADLs). Activities of daily living typically include bathing, dressing, mobility, toileting, continence, and eating. It is estimated that 60% of people living today will need care in an assisted living facility. The average monthly cost in the U.S. is more than $3,600 for a one-bedroom unit.

- **Skilled Nursing Facility/Nursing Home Care:** When a person is unable to receive care at home or in an assisted living facility, he/she will receive care in a nursing home or memory care unit. This type of care is the most specialized – and the most expensive type of care. It is estimated that 43% of people living today will need care in a skilled nursing facility. The average cost in the U.S. is nearly $7,000/month for a semi-private room.

Who Pays for LTC?

Many consumers mistakenly believe their health or disability insurance will cover the cost of care in any of these housing situations. They won't. Nor will a government program like Medicare or Medicaid. Others assume that family members will provide their care, but this can place a potentially significant burden on sons and daughters who have careers and families of their own.

In reality, there are only two ways to pay for long-term care costs:

- You pay for those costs out of your own pocket.
- You purchase long-term care insurance so the insurance company pays those expenses.

Let's examine each of those options closely:

- **You will pay for long-term care expenses out of your own pocket.**
  - With costs ranging between $50,000 per year for assisted living and $84,000 for a semi-private nursing home bed, how long can the average person afford to pay those bills until they run out of money? For most Americans, the answer is, "Not long." Once you run out of money – in Arizona, your assets can't exceed $2,205 -- the state will pick up the cost of care for you through its Medicaid program (Arizona Health Care Cost Containment System). However, once you go on Medicaid, you lose all control over the type of care you receive and where you will receive that care. Rest assured that the state does not have your best interests in mind when they make long-term care choices for you.

- **You purchase long-term care insurance so the insurance company pays those expenses.**
    - ° When you purchase long-term care insurance, you maintain control of your care. You choose where you receive that care, how much care you want to receive, and who will give that care to you.
    - ° When you purchase long-term care insurance, you protect your assets. Since the insurance company is paying the expenses, your assets are not depleted and you can protect your estate. Many states, including Arizona, participate in the Long-Term Care Partnership Program, which protects the value of your estate up to the value of your long-term care policy coverage. How it works: You have a long-term care policy with coverage up to $250,000 for a 3-year benefit period. After you use up your entire 3 years of care you need to dip into personal savings and/or assets to continue paying for your care. Say you only have $50,000 in savings – a small amount considering the high cost of care. Because you have a LTC policy, your personal assets are protected up to $250,000, which means the government is still obliged to cover your care under the Medicaid program without touching that $50,000. Without a LTC policy, you would have to exhaust your assets in order to reach the level where you could draw on Medicaid benefits. So, a long-term care policy protects your wealth.

Do I Really Need Long-Term Care Insurance?

It is wise to plan for long-term care for several reasons, among them the high cost of that care.

As also noted earlier, many consumers assume their children will take care of them when they need it. While many children are happy to do so, it may be bring many unintended consequences along with it:

Caregiving is a tedious and exhausting challenge for a family. I have seen many situations where children have become seriously ill as a result of caring for aging parents. The result is that the children's family situation is then severely stressed due to the caregiving and the children's family then ends up in severe financial or emotional or physical distress.

I have also seen situations where loving children try to care for their parents but during that process become angry or embittered toward their parents due to the stress of caregiving. Once those parents pass away, the memories the children have are not of the good times they shared but often the years of anger and fights, unpleasant bathroom experiences, and irritability in general.

This isn't the legacy most of us want to leave behind.

A long-term care policy enables a family to leave caregiving to professionals who are trained and suited for that task. It enables a family to keep pleasant memories of parents and loved ones and shifts the caregiving stress to someone outside the family who has no emotional connections to the situation and can objectively provide the best care with the least minimum impact on family members.

Having a long-term care policy enables you to be in charge of your own care.

When you purchase a long-term care policy, you have freedom to dictate how and where you want to receive long-term care, and by whom.

If you prefer to stay in your own home as long as possible, you can purchase a long-term care policy that covers in-home health care. If you don't, you may be paying more than $150 per day for assistance. For 24-hour care, the cost is around $500 per day.

Some home health care agencies may discount the 24-hour price, but at that point, it would be less expensive for the person to receive care in an assisted living facility.

When Do I Get Coverage?

Generally, the specific circumstance that causes a long-term care claim to be paid is referred to as a "benefit trigger" or "qualification trigger." As a result of the Health Insurance Portability and Accountability Act of 1996 (HIPPA), long-term care policies will require either that you are either cognitively impaired or you need substantial assistance with two or more activities of daily living (ADLs) to trigger benefits. In most long-term care policies, the trigger is the same for home health care, assisted living, or nursing home care.

"The time to repair the roof is when the sun is shining" -John F. Kennedy

ADLs are typically listed as bathing, dressing, mobility, eating, toileting, and continence.

A few useful definitions:

Cognitive impairment can include anything like dementia, Alzheimer's disease, a closed-head injury, etc. To trigger LTC benefits, your impairment must reach the level where your health or safety are at risk. My mother-in-law, for example, had memory problems, but she was able to live by herself without needing or requiring any assistance. Then her doctor told us that he was afraid that if she left her apartment she would not find her way back in; the illness had reached a point where my mother-in-law could have used her LTC policy.

Substantial assistance with two or more ADLs means you require "hands-on" help.

How Do I File a Claim with a LTC Policy?

The first step is to contact the claims department of the insurance company. At that point, many insurance companies will order an assessment. The assessment can be done in your home if you are in need of home health care, or an assessment can be done in an assisted living facility or nursing home if you or your caregiver is living outside the home in some type of facility.

Once an assessment is ordered, the patient is given a memory test to determine cognitive impairment levels, or he/she is observed to determine ability to perform ADLs. In either case, the results of the assessment are then sent to the claims department of the insurance company to determine if the person qualifies for a claim to be paid.

When Should I Buy a Long-Term Care Policy?

The best time to purchase a long-term care policy is when you are still relatively young and in good health.

- **Age:** Premiums are based on age, so the younger the applicant, the lower the premium. Many people feel that it would be better to delay purchasing a long-term care policy until their 70's because they would pay premiums for less time than if they purchased a policy in their 40's or 50's. However, if you calculate the premiums out over time, a person would pay less in premiums if they purchase a long-term care policy in their 40' or 50's than they would if they waited until their 70's, when rates are much higher. The older we are, the more health problems we tend to have. Therefore, the longer you wait to apply for long-term care coverage, the less likely you are to be approved for coverage due to increasing health issues and concerns.

The best age to apply for long-term care is generally between ages 45 and 55. Between those ages, the premiums are lowest due to age and minimal health concerns. That is not to say that a person in their 70's or 80's cannot qualify for a long-term care policy. It simply means that a person in their 70's and 80's is likely to have more health problems and statistically less likely to qualify for coverage.

- **Health:** Long-term care insurance has extensive underwriting, which means that the insurance company will check your medical history to see whether or not they want to insure you for long-term care. Insurance companies may decide to offer coverage but charge a higher premium based on a person's health history. Or, the company may decline to offer a policy at all if they are not comfortable covering a person for the long haul.

For example, diabetes is a chronic disease that worsens as a person ages. Consequently, people with diabetes have a high likelihood of needing long-term care at some point in their lives. Thus, the insurance premium may be higher. A person with complications from diabetes (such as peripheral neuropathy or retinopathy) would likely be declined for coverage.

How is a Long-Term Care Policy Structured?

There are many variables that make up the coverage and ultimately the cost of a long-term care policy. In addition to the individual applicant's age and health, the following options for coverage are major determining factors in the premium charged:

Benefit Amount: Once the claim starts, this is the amount that the insurance company will pay for care. Benefits can be figured on a daily ($100/day) or a monthly ($3000) basis. The range typically varies between $50/day ($1500/month) up to $400/day ($12,000/month). Obviously, the higher the benefit amount, the higher the premium.

Benefit Period: Once the claim starts, this is the length of time or total dollar amount that the insurance company will pay for care over the lifetime of the claim. A benefit period can be written in dollar amounts ($36,000-$600,000) or in length of years (2-6 years). The longer the benefit period or the higher the dollar amount, the higher the premium.

Elimination Period: The elimination period is one of the most misunderstood parts of a long-term care policy. The elimination period is a deductible. It is written in number of days (0, 30, 60, 90, 180, etc.) and is the time frame in which the insurance company is eliminated from having to pay on the claim. Thus the insured pays the full cost of care during that time period. So, if you had a 90 day elimination period, the insured would pay the full cost of care for the first 90 days and then, beginning on the 91st day, the insurance company would begin payments. The longer the elimination period, the lower the premium.

Inflation Rider: It is possible to add an inflation rider to the benefit amount so the benefit amount will increase over time. The most common inflation riders are simple or compound with rates ranging anywhere from 1% to 5%. The higher the interest rate, the higher the premium.

All of the variables defined above, as well as an individual's age and health, figure into determining the long-term care premium. Premiums can be paid on a monthly, quarterly, semi-annual, or annual basis. Many companies also have additional discounts if both spouses apply for coverage.

Long-term care insurance today

Long-term care insurance has evolved with the demands of an aging population. One very positive development was the creation of a long-term care partnership which Arizona, as well as a number of other states, offer to individuals. The way it works: if you buy a long-term care policy that meets partnership specifications, you can deduct a portion of the long-term care premiums on your taxes -- as long the policy meets those specifications. Partnership policies are also guaranteed renewable and provide for nonforfeiture benefits if you default on the payment of premiums.

Traditional long-term care policies have come under fire due to the possibility of rate increases over time -- and the fact that if you don't need long-term care, you've paid a hefty sum over the years that you can't recover. That's where two new categories of LTC "hybrid" policies fit in.

Hybrid policies

The first category of LTC hybrid policies is a life insurance policy that also offers long-term care benefits, usually through a policy rider. So, if you have a $100,000 policy with a LTC rider and you need the money to pay for care associated with a chronic illness, you could withdraw a percentage of the money. Policy premiums do not increase as they do with standard LTC policies. It is easier to qualify – even with a preexisting condition. If you die without drawing on the long-term care benefits, the death benefit goes to your estate. If you have withdrawn money for care, the value of the death benefit is reduced by that amount.

The second type of hybrid policy is an annuity with a long-term care rider. In this scenario, you deposit a sum of money (usually $50,000 minimum) into an annuity which has a long-term care rider. Like most annuities, the money deposited grows over time. If you or a loved one needs long-term care, you can withdraw a portion of that money without penalty each year to pay for long-term care needs. Since this is an annuity and a one-time lump sum deposit is made, there are no rate increases. If you or a loved one dies without needing long-term care, the value of the annuity is paid out to the estate. This type of product is great for those who have serious health issues and would not qualify for a typical long-term care policy, because no medical questions are asked on the application. The individual is purchasing an annuity and, consequently, health is not one of the considerations for the applicant.

As a broker, I have never heard a family member express regret that a loved one had a long-term care policy – even if the policy was minimal in coverage. There was at least some financial help in paying bills.

SOURCE:

Genworth Cost of Care Survey, 2016: https://www. genworth.com/about-us/industry-expertise/cost-of-care. html.

10

Where There's A Will, There's A Way

By Timothy Holt, managing attorney, TrustLawyers, PLLC

> "Estate planning is an important and everlasting gift you can give your family. And setting up a smooth inheritance isn't as hard as you might think."
>
> **Suze Orman**

Estate planning is the process of making provisions to:

- Protect our families if we can no longer do so
- Provide for our own needs if we are incapacitated by injury or disease
- Wind up our lives and define our legacy

This process typically involves financial arrangements, long-term care decisions, identifying the needs of those we love and for whom we care, and making the best use of all the capital (both financial and social) that we have accumulated during our lives.

No Will or Trust?

If you have no will or trust, the Arizona legislature has its own plan for you—given through the "interstate succession" statutes. This is how the state decides what happens to your property, and it is as bad as it sounds. Some call it divorce court for the dead. Do you know anyone that had a bad experience in divorce court? For example, if you die without a will and you are married, your surviving spouse gets everything. If there are children prior to the marriage, your spouse still gets everything. If there is at least one child from a prior marriage or relationship, your surviving spouse gets one third of your estate and that child or children gets two-thirds of your estate. Probably not what you intended.

Many people think that you only go to probate court if you don't have a will. Actually, a will is your ticket to probate. The will must be filed and accepted by the court before your personal representative (executor) can do anything. If you live in Maricopa County, get in line: There are only two probate judges in the county who are assisted by five probate court commissioners. Together, these seven judicial officers are responsible for about 30,000 pending cases. According to Maricopa County, many of these probate cases are still pending after several years. If you don't have a trust, you will eventually be in this mess.

Unfortunately, most people find that their lives are driven by events. They may think about being proactive, but it just seems easier to react to things as they happen. In the area of estate planning, however, there is no second chance. It is time to get proactive.

The Purpose Statement

Let's talk about one vitally important area that most attorneys don't even address: creating a Purpose Statement for your trust.

A well-drafted trust allows you to leave directions, not directives. It's critical to create an understandable statement of what you really want your trust to accomplish for your heirs, for the charities you may support, and any other beneficiary you may choose. For example, you may want to encourage and support family growth and happiness. What about providing tools for financial education? Reinforcing your values is entirely appropriate, as could be emphasizing sharing with others. The most important thing about your purpose clause is simply that it is *yours*. You know better than anyone else what is important to you and what will be of most benefit to your family.

A skilled estate planner knows how to help you create a meaningful purpose clause.

Pretend that you have just learned that you only have a few minutes to live. You have time to place a call to each of your children and to spend 15 minutes with each of them. In addition to telling them how much you love them, what could you compress into that 15-minute conversation that would be of lasting value to them?

Simple statements in a trust which capture a parent's or grandparent's love, faith, and hope, for and in the beneficiary, create a genuine emotional attachment to the document. The best legacy you can leave is probably not financial. Passing on your knowledge and values is worth infinitely more because it can provide positive direction and encouragement to your children and grandchildren as they go forward without you.

What if you included something like one or all of the following: Reflections about the day my child was born, how we chose your name and what it meant to us, memories of trips or vacations when we created priceless memories, things I have always admired about you, special talents or gifts I feel you have been given and the great potential I have seen in you, really difficult challenges I have seen you overcome and how I felt about your effort, things you said or did for me which really made me feel special or loved, how I felt when you reached and passed important milestones in your life such as high school or college graduation, your first big job, favorite quotes or life lessons I think may be important to you or your children in the future, things you probably never heard me talk about which made life special or were particularly challenging or difficult.

What about the name of your trust? The name you choose for your trust should reflect your own purposes, hopes, and dreams. It can be a link allowing you to connect both your family and your trustee to your intent in creating the gift that is your trust. Whenever your trustee makes a decision, and every time your beneficiary gets a check, he or she will be reminded of your hopes for them. The name you choose can define your legacy for years to come. What kind of name will meaningfully impact your loved ones. It may take you some time to reach a decision, but it will be one of the most meaningful components of your estate plan. Recently a client of mine set up a trust to benefit the children of her only son, who was deceased. His name was Jared, and her trust is the 'Jared Legacy Trust'. This will be a constant, loving reminder to her grandchildren of her love for their father.

Beneficiary Designations

How do you name a beneficiary or beneficiaries? This is a key item we discuss when people come to us to have their estate plan prepared.

When you set up a life insurance policy or annuity or IRA, you will be asked to name a beneficiary. Some types of financial products also allow you to name a beneficiary such as a 'pay on death' or 'transfer on death' designation.

These beneficiary designations? They trump both the state statutes that normally control when you die with or without a will or trust.

What?

Yes, if your will says everything goes to your kids, but your ex's name is still on the 401(k) plan as the beneficiary, your ex is going to get it. That's the law of the land. Make sure you've updated your beneficiary designations on your financial accounts.

The Disability Contingency

As poet Robert Burns mused centuries ago, "The best-laid plans of mice and men often go awry."

Despite thoughtful effort and a concerted strategy, you cannot prepare for every emergency. A car accident, sudden illness, workplace injury, or chronic medical condition can force you to re-evaluate the core assumptions you used to plan your future and set up your legacy.

It's important to prepare for disability by working with your financial advisor to make sure you and your family are fully protected.

Frustratingly, you can't turn back the clock. You can, however, take meaningful actions to protect your legacy and estate in the wake of newfound limitations. To that end, I suggest you work with a qualified estate planning attorney to ensure the following:

- There's an authorized person to make financial and healthcare decisions for you if you become mentally or physically unable to do so yourself.
- There's also an authorized person to manage your property, pay your bills, file your taxes, and handle similar business if you're unable to do these tasks.
- Your wishes about health care decisions, such as end of life care and do-not-resuscitate instructions, have been communicated in a legally valid and binding manner.
- You get a recommendation from your estate planning attorney or your financial advisor, who can help you take additional actions, such as ensuring that you have appropriate insurance, reassessing your investment options and portfolio in light of your new limitations and constraints on your ability to generate income, and making sure that you have a budget that works and that your bills will all get paid on time.

The Evolving State of Estate Planning

Estate planning has truly evolved over the past 20 years. Gone is the uncertainty about federal estate taxes and the absolute requirement for married couples to use complex trusts to minimize these taxes. But also gone is planning for the "traditional" family. In 1995 the federal estate tax exemption was only $600,000 and the estate tax rate was 55%. Back then it was easy to accumulate a taxable estate by simply owning a home, a few investments, and some life insurance. And while married couples could pass on two times the exemption ($1.2 million) free from estate taxes if they incorporated Marital/Family Trusts into their estate plan, these trusts came with strings attached. Yet these inflexible trusts were worth it to avoid the hefty 55% tax on assets valued over $600,000.

Avoiding costly probate was another concern 20 years ago. No longer was a Last Will and Testament that required oversight by a probate court the preferred document for passing assets on to heirs. Instead the ultimate probate-avoidance tool, the revocable living trust, became all the rage. Fast forward 20 years, and in 2016 the federal estate tax exemption is a whopping $5.45 million and will continue to increase annually based on inflation. In addition, between 2002 and 2013 the federal estate tax rate dropped from 55% to 40%.

Today, the focus of estate planning has shifted away from estate tax planning and probate avoidance to more relevant concerns.

Today, many families are also blended, dysfunctional, or completely estranged. This has made flexible estate planning and finding ways to modify what was thought to be an irrevocable plan the 'new normal.'

As a result, traditional Marital/Family Trust planning is no longer a necessity for the majority of families. In fact, an older

> While the federal estate tax rate has declined from 55% to 40%, since 2012, the top federal income tax rate has increased from 35% to 43.4%, and the top long-term capital gains rate has increased from 15% to 23.8%. Some irrevocable trusts might pay these high tax rates. This has made minimizing income taxes an integral part of estate planning.

> Higher income tax rates, changing state laws, unfavorable jurisdictions, and wayward heirs all add up to the need for an estate plan that will be able to adapt over time. Modern families need modern estate planning solutions.

Marital/Family Trust plan will lead to an unnecessary income tax liability for heirs since the assets of the Family Trust will not receive a stepup in basis. Therefore, instead of planning for excluding assets from the taxable estate, the new trend for couples with less than $10 million is to plan for estate inclusion so that their heirs will receive a basis stepup.

In conclusion, the most important steps to take are as follows:

- Admit to yourself that you need to do this.
- Commit to finding the right person to help you, and don't be afraid to interview more than one person.
- Focus on value, not cost. You need to be sure that the attorney you retain is knowledgeable and has the skills to make your goals achievable. Remember, you are not in the market to buy documents. You are looking for a well thought-out solution that is customized for your family. Otherwise you might as well go to the office supply store and buy a $30 will kit, fill it out, and be done.
- Get the help you need from multiple trusted family members, friends, and professionals. No single advisor will have all the answers. Build a team that can work in concert to reduce the anxiety and uncertainty and keep you focused on what really matters.

Each of us can make that 'last gift' – a will or trust – not just a list of things and money to be doled out to our family and loved ones. Taking the bull by the horns and making sure that we have done all that we can will not only leave us with peace of mind, but it will create a very real legacy for generations to come.

SOURCES:

Maricopa County Superior Court Probate Court Department: "Case Management Improvement Plan For Adult Guardianship and Conservatorship Cases."

Forbes.com: "Probate, Wills, Executors: Your Estate Planning Questions Answered," April 7, 2017.

11

Minding The Piggy Bank: Planning Your Financial Future

By Marc Giannone, Retirement Income Certified Professional®

When I talk to families about their finances, many feel hopelessly confused. They don't know if they've saved enough. They don't know how to protect what they have saved. They don't know the best way to invest. They don't know when they can consider retiring. They don't know how to create an income for themselves in retirement. The list goes on. The families I've met simply lack confidence in their financial future, and because it's overwhelming to think about it they do very little to remedy the situation.

Over the years, the unfortunate reality of financial planning has been that more emphasis is placed on the "how" of reaching your financial goals rather than identifying and developing the financial goals themselves. We've been led to believe that the most important components of creating a bright and confident financial future are

> "If you don't know where you're going, you'll end up someplace else." -Yogi Berra

making sure you buy enough insurance, find investments that beat the stock market benchmarks, or have some fancy trust drawn up by your attorney. These couldn't be further from the truth.

As someone who considers it a privilege and weighty responsibility to help families create a bright and confident financial future, I find it heartbreaking that the financial industry has let down hard-working families in this regard. According to the Employee Benefit Research Institute's 2016 Retirement Confidence Survey, just 21% of workers are confident they will have enough money in retirement. The financial industry has overcomplicated a straightforward process, and confused it by making it all about products.

I'd like to set a few things straight. In doing so, hopefully you will discover that financial planning can give you the clarity you've been looking for so you can *Age in Arizona*, knowing full well that you have a bright and confident financial future ahead of you.

Let's cut through all the mumbo jumbo and get down to the bare bones of financial planning. Plain and simple, financial planning is about painting a very clear picture about your current financial situation, defining a few clear goals about where you want to go, and developing a road map to get from where you are to where you want to be -- period. Sure, there's a lot that goes into getting us from Point A to Point B, but it's crucial that we start with the end in mind. How could we possibly decide what to do if we haven't thought about why we're doing it? Let me be clear: earning a high rate of return is *not* a financial goal. Making a reasonable rate of return so that you have accumulated a specific sum of money to live off in your golden years is a financial goal.

See the difference?

It used to be, maybe in your parents' or grandparents' time, people worked for the same employer for decades, building a retirement egg paycheck by paycheck. They knew they would have a pension on the other side.

Times have changed. Companies have discontinued offering employees a traditional pension benefit because of the corresponding payment liabilities, and have instead shifted the responsibility and risk back to the employees by making them responsible for saving and investing through investment vehicles like 401(k) or 403(b) plans. This is a big deal.

Many workers can't look forward to a pension or any kind of post-retirement benefit – and we have a failing Social Security fund, which serves as the primary source of funds for many Americans.

Although I don't expect the system to completely disappear anytime soon, it's reasonable to speculate that there will need to be changes in the future to sustain the continuation of the system. Whether

> "Good fortune is what happens when opportunity meets with planning." -Thomas Edison

it be increasing the "full retirement age," reducing benefits for high-income earners, raising taxes, or some combination of sorts, Social Security will likely not provide the same level of security to future generations as it has recently. Because of this shift in responsibility from the employer and government to the individual, our working population MUST plan for the future if they want to be able to one day stop working for a paycheck.

We have an amazing opportunity to build wealth that serves to strengthen our families and the causes we care about, but without planning the opportunity will be lost.

I am going to address retirement planning for middle-aged and older adults here, with the hope you'll try to avoid a quick fix to live out your years in relative comfort.

Let's consider a hypothetical example: For years, "Jim and Carol" worked hard to provide their family with what we'd consider the American Dream. They owned a home, lived in a nice neighborhood, had two vehicles, and took an annual vacation to the beach.

As the years passed and the kids made their way through grade school, Jim and Carol continued to delay retirement savings until one day, the kids were out of the house, retirement age was in sight, and they had little saved. Jim and Carol always thought they would retire at age 60, 65 if necessary. They envisioned traveling, spending time with their grandkids, and volunteering with their church's missions team.

It was clear after a brief conversation with them that their expectations for retirement didn't align with their current reality. As we continued our discussion, my objective was not to destroy their dreams of retirement but to bring perspective and be realistic about how to achieve their goals. After gaining a sense of their current state of affairs, I took out a piece of blank paper and started sketching an outline of how we might meet their income needs.

There are several strategies to plan for retirement income, and the strategy depends on the individual and his or her circumstances. But the "flooring approach" is one that seeks to match essential expenses (such as food, shelter, healthcare, transportation, etc.) with fixed sources of income such as Social Security, pensions, and even immediate annuities.

Again, every family is different; therefore, strategies and investment vehicles vary. For Jim and Carol, we crafted a retirement income plan that they felt gave them the peace of mind they needed, knowing that their essential (floor) expenses would be covered. By doing so, we could think differently about how to cover the remaining discretionary expenses (i.e. vacations, gifting, etc.).

Monies they had saved above and beyond what was needed to generate the "floor" was considered longer-term money that would cover discretionary expenses. We identified a safe withdrawal rate at which they could spend from those assets annually. Because they still had a few years before retirement, the additional savings they would accumulate over the next few years would go toward building those assets.

Throughout this process, Jim and Carol had a few "ah-ha" moments. When we sat down and calculated exactly how much they needed to sustain their basic needs (their "floor"), they were blown away. Knowing exactly how much that monthly number was brought confidence to them that, if the worst happened, they could still survive because their fixed income sources (Social Security, a small pension, and an annuity) were enough to cover those expenses. One of the first decisions we made together, even before creating the income plan, was to set aside an emergency reserve. This simple concept of keeping a certain amount of money set aside in cash gave them the peace of mind of having a level of protection if unforeseen emergency expenses came up that couldn't be covered by their regular money income. Although that may sound elementary, you'd be surprised just how many families wouldn't be able to cover just a few weeks of expenses if their income stopped.

When we calculated the current cost of their dream retirement and applied a reasonable inflation rate, they finally felt like they had the information needed to make some tough decisions and get back on track toward meeting their goals.

None of this sounds very complicated, does it? It's not. But it takes time, intention, planning, and discipline.

Post-retirement financial challenges

Now to the financial challenges that face adults who are long past retirement and their families. Much of it will be in healthcare costs.

Recent research from Fidelity finds that a couple who retired in 2015, both age 65, could expect to spend an estimated $245,000 on healthcare throughout their retirement. That's up significantly from $220,000 in 2014 and $190,000 in 2005.

Our life expectancy has increased by nearly 20 years over the last century – American men who reach age 65 have a 1-in-4 chance of living to 92. American women reaching 65 have a 1-in-4 chance of living to 94.2. That's close to a 30-year retirement!

Although living longer sounds good, it also means we need to make our retirement savings last longer. And that's no easy task given that pesky little thing called inflation, which sneaks up on us slowly but surely at a historical rate of about 3.5% per year. At that rate, you can expect goods and services will cost twice as much 20 years from now. Put another way, one of the biggest challenges facing the elderly and their families is that of preserving purchasing power, not necessarily principle as most assume. All the more reason to spend the time and effort necessary to take an assessment of how to craft a retirement income plan that will give you the best probability of not running out of money when you need it most.

If we've planned and prepared well for the future, we have lots to look forward to.

Here are some recommendations:

Get VERY organized and crystal clear about what your goals are now and what they need to be in the future. Once you know what the needs are, you can work to put together an income plan that meets those goals. There are various tools that will allow you to meet these goals, and I could go on for chapters about each of them. However, like building a house, the most important part is putting the time and effort in upfront with a qualified architect and contractor to lay out the blue print. Deciding upon the various building materials is secondary.

Be transparent with your family about your financial concerns and desires. It's better to have those discussions early on than to surprise them when it's too late. I've seen families ripped apart due to lack of communication about financial desires. Be transparent with your children, especially if they're going to be the ones responsible for handling your affairs when you're unable to do so yourself.

In conclusion, it's not too late to plan. Whether you're 55, planning for your own retirement, and attending to the needs of aging parents, or whether you're 95 and enjoying your golden years,

> "The time to repair the roof is when the sun is shining" -John F. Kennedy

there's no time like now to get organized, set clear goals about what you want for yourself and family, and seek out solutions to get you from where you are today to where you want to be tomorrow.

DISCLAIMER

Eaton-Cambridge Inc. is a State Registered Investment Adviser. Information presented is for educational purposes only and should not be construed as investment advice as the information may not be suitable for all investors. The information does not intend to make an offer or solicitation for the sale or purchase of any specific securities, investments, or investment strategies. Investments involve risk and, unless otherwise stated, are not guaranteed. Eaton-Cambridge Inc. does not provide legal or tax advice. Be sure to first consult with a qualified financial adviser and/or tax professional before implementing any strategy discussed herein. Past performance is not indicative of future performance.

SOURCES:

Employee Benefit Research Institute: 2016 Retirement Confidence Survey.

Fidelity: "Health Care Costs for Couples in Retirement Rise to an Estimated $245,000," Oct. 7, 2015.

Society of Actuaries: Annuity 2000 Mortality Table.

Centers for Disease Control: National Center for Health Statistics, National Vital Statistics Reports.

12

THE HOSPICE EMBRACE

By Rhea Go-Coloma, LMSW, CMFSW, chief
administrative officer of Hospice of the West

> "I wonder if my first breath was as soul-stirring to
> my mother as her last breath was to me."
>
> From 14 Days: *A Mother, A Daughter, A Two-Week
> Goodbye* by Lisa Goich-Andreadis

The History and Philosophy of Hospice

When hospice was developed in the 1960s by UK physician
Dame Cicely Saunders, it was built on a foundation and spirit of
remembering to give the terminally ill the right to choose how they want to die. The priority for hospice was to empower and assist patients to participate in decisions that affect their care.

> "We live in a very particular death-denying society. We isolate both the dying and the old, and it serves a purpose. They are reminders of our own mortality. We should not institutionalize people. We can give families more help with home care and visiting nurses, giving the families and the patients the spiritual, emotional, and financial help in order to facilitate the final care at home." -On Death and Dying by Elizabeth Kubler-Ross, hospice pioneer

107

Today, hospice professionals remain committed to help the dying determine what matters to them most when they are in their final days, weeks, or months of life. When an individual has opted to be under the care of hospice, he or she is entrusting others to the most precious, intimate memories and moments of their life. It is truly a privilege for hospice to be a witness, a companion, and a chosen confidante in celebration of a life being lived.

Hospice is not a place, but rather a philosophy of care. Hospice care is available 24 hours a day, seven days a week. The interdisciplinary hospice team is available after office hours and on weekends to provide compassionate care and support at the patient's place of residence, which is wherever the patient considers home. Patients may reside in skilled nursing facilities, assisted living homes and communities, retirement and independent living communities, in a private home, or in another unique type of setting such as a homeless shelter. Hospice offers short-term inpatient care for patients who require around-the-clock skilled nursing care for pain and symptom management. Hospice also provides respite care for patients who need a place to go to for care so that their family members may have a short break from caregiving.

What is Hospice Care?

A person who is eligible for hospice services receives the following individualized care from a committed, competent, caring, and compassionate interdisciplinary team of professionals who are available anytime – day or night.

- Physicians/medical directors oversee all plans of care, facilitates interdisciplinary team meetings, conduct home visits as required by the care plan, and work with the patient's primary care physicians/specialists to provide a continuum of care.

- Skilled nurses/case managers coordinate the delivery of care. The nurse is an extension of the physician, to provide quality nursing care, pain and symptom management, and make arrangements for medications, medical equipment, and supplies. The skilled nurse offers education on the diagnosis, prognosis, disease process, and dying process.
- Hospice aides assist with personal care needs such as bathing and grooming. They also assist with the activities of daily living of the patient, such as ambulating, dressing, and feeding. Hospice aides assist caregivers with linen changes. They can also provide complimentary therapies such as range of motion, and meaningful touch.
- Social workers offer psychosocial support and assist with a multitude of areas, such as navigating through the healthcare system, resolving legal and financial issues, advanced care planning, mortuary planning, placement, mediation of family dynamics, and coordination of additional community support and resources. The social worker provides education and guidance to help patients and families in end-of-life matters.
- Chaplains offer spiritual support and provide reflective discussion of religion and faith. They assist in the discussion of spiritual concerns, connect family with their faith community, and may assist in planning of the patient's memorial service.
- Volunteers offer their time and talents to provide conversation and/or companionship and support to patients and families in a variety of special activities or

meaningful presence. They may assist with errands, light housekeeping, and light meal preparation. They may also provide short respite breaks to the caregivers and family members.

- Bereavement counselors offer grief support to caregivers and family members after the death of a patient. They may provide pre-bereavement support prior to a patient's death if necessary, and can provide one-on-one counseling and support groups, if desired.

Who Pays for Hospice?

Hospice care is covered by Medicare for those individuals who have a life-limiting illness, as confirmed by a physician, and meet the eligibility criteria for end-of-life care under Medicare guidelines. A physician must certify that a person's life expectancy is six months or less. This time frame can be extended beyond the six months as long as the individual continues to meet hospice eligibility and if the symptoms are related to his or her terminal illness.

Hospice care is also covered by some AHCCCS (Arizona Health Care Cost Containment System, the state's Medicaid agency) plans and most insurance plans. In addition to physician, nursing, hospice aide, social work, chaplain, bereavement, and volunteer services, the medications, medical equipment and supplies, short-term inpatient and respite care stays, complementary therapies (physical, occupational and speech) are covered under Medicare as long as the need is related to the patient's hospice diagnosis.

Planning for Hospice Care

Discussing end-of-life care can be overwhelming, scary, and difficult, but it doesn't have to be. Learning about hospice early can reduce a lot of worry, stress, and confusion.

Families often share that they don't know when it is time for hospice, but it is vital that the hospice conversation begin early

> "Thank you so much for being there in our time of need. I can move on with my life knowing we did everything we could for my father in his final day. Without your help and guidance, it would have been a challenge. My father passed with dignity and, without your help, it may not have happened as gracefully as it did. Thank you" -E.M.R., a resident of Sun City, AZ

so individuals and their families know how the hospice philosophy of care can benefit them. It is time to call when it has been determined that there is no cure for an illness, when the person with the life-limiting illness decides to stop seeking aggressive treatment, or when his or her health is progressively declining despite treatment.

Julie is a prime example of how hospice can help an individual live a life of quality while faced with a life-limiting illness.

Julie came to hospice with end-stage liver disease and was told by her physician she only had a short time to live. When she first was admitted into hospice, she was grieving this diagnosis and prognosis. She regretted some of her past life decisions that had led to her poor health and alienated her from her family. She had limited contact with her only adult son who was far across the country serving in the Air Force.

When the hospice team became involved, Julie had recently transitioned from a skilled nursing facility, where she was unhappy, to a small apartment with limited caregivers to assist her. Unfortunately, she received poor care from these caregivers, which added to her frustration, sadness, and disempowerment. Julie felt she had gotten lost in a system that had some prejudice against her, given her past choices.

The hospice social worker began the process of validating Julie's ongoing struggles as a result of her many health challenges.

By 2020, the number of people living with at least one chronic illness will increase to 157 million. Today, seven out of 10 Americans die from chronic disease.

> By 2020, the number of people living with at least one chronic illness will increase to 157 million. Today seven out of 10 Americans die from chronic disease.

The team also worked hard to customize her medication regimen to manage her symptoms, such as nausea and pain. From time to time, she required a brief hospital visit to have a paracentesis, a procedure that extracts fluid from a person's abdomen. The collaboration between hospice and other providers helped keep Julie comfortable.

The hospice team also worked hard to advocate on Julie's behalf since her family members were in another state. The team empowered Julie and educated her on her patient rights, guiding her as she made important decisions about her care. This included financial and legal matters, such as applying for Arizona Long-Term Care System (ALTCS) benefits. The social worker was able to assist her in completing her advanced directives and other important documents that let her family know her thoughts and feelings. As a result of the assistance, Julie could focus on becoming a person her son could respect.

The hospice interdisciplinary team supported Julie as her health continued to decline, even pulling together resources to furnish her home. During this time, Julie worked on her relationship with her son. He expressed deep gratitude to the hospice team for treating her with such care and dignity and for giving him peace of mind. Eventually, the hospice team was able to assist Julie reunite with her son, who is now actively involved with her care.

The Hospice Embrace

Hospice professionals are often told by a family member of a dying loved one, "Why did we wait so long to call hospice? I wish we had called sooner." Many come to realize that, if hospice were involved sooner, the patient and family would have received a level of care and support that would have remarkably improved the overall healthcare experience for the patient and their support network. This is an important reason why hospice can and should be understood and discussed before it is needed. It is important that older adults and family members have an opportunity to dialogue about all types of health care options with providers and one another.

When a person is ready for hospice care, medical eligibility is important, but so is being able to mentally and emotionally accept the service. Hospice professionals are available to guide and support individuals and their families through their thoughts and feelings, as well as assist them in gaining an understanding of patient rights, responsibilities, benefits, and services. The most important information to remember is that hospice is a choice. Should a patient decide that they would like to go back to seeking aggressive, curative care, they may revoke their hospice benefit. Should the patient want to return to hospice care in the future, they have the option of being re-evalued and re-admitted, if appropriate. It is always the patient's choice. The hospice team will honor the right for patients to self-determine by providing honest and respectful information.

According to a 2010 study in the *New England Journal of Medicine*, patients receiving early palliative care experienced less depression, had better quality of life, and survived 2.7 months longer.

If hospice care is a possible option, the patient, family, or legal representative should also have a conversation with the patient's primary care physician or other trusted health care workers (case manager, social worker, guardian, fiduciary, nurse, etc.), asking about their prognosis, and discussing goals of care.

Most often, a healthcare provider or an advocate can provide a patient and their family with referrals to hospices. Patients and their medical powers of attorney have the right to choose to meet with more than one hospice. A patient and their support network should call their hospice of choice and request to speak to a hospice professional such as an intake coordinator or hospice liaison. A hospice presentation and evaluation will be scheduled so that a hospice nurse or representative can personally provide detailed education on hospice and offer caring guidance through the evaluation process.

The importance of hospice can be challenging to describe unless one has experienced this compassionate and comprehensive model of care.

"This is such a difficult time in a person's life—both for the one who is dying and for those who love them. You have eased this difficult time and I will never forget what all of you have done for us and meant to us."
~J.F., Resident of Sun City, AZ, as told to Hospice of the West

Unfortunately, there are a lot of misconceptions about hospice, including the philosophy of care and services. Not all healthcare providers are educated on having the hospice conversation. A primary goal for hospice is to debunk common myths and to guide others in having an open, honest, healthy discussion on what hospice is.

An example of a common myth is hospice means giving up hope. The truth is that deciding to receive hospice services does not mean giving up hope. Hospice is about redefining the patient's goals. The hope may have transitioned from curing the illness to the hope of living life to its fullest when one has a life-limiting illness. Once a patient is receiving hospice services they sometimes will feel a greater sense of overall well-being. From being involved in the day-to-day decisions of their plan of care, to relief from pain and other symptoms, to having emotional support for themselves and their families, patients are able to live lives of a higher quality, with moments of meaningful reflection and fulfillment.

I'd like to conclude with a letter we received from a patient's family. I believe their words express most clearly and powerfully the importance of understanding hospice care and the value that it can provide:

"It is with great love, admiration, and gratitude that I am sending this letter to all of you. My mother had been in your care for quite some time, especially since the deaths of both my sisters earlier this year. During that time you had cared for her, she was comfortable, happy, pain-free, and at peace. She loved you all and prayed for you every day. I am sure she is still praying for all of you and asking God to bless you for the wonderful care you provided her. I want to extend my personal thanks to every doctor, nurse, hospice aide, and the office staff that answered my calls, and anyone else who came into contact with us. Your care, gentleness, kindness, and above all, your love and respect did not go unnoticed by her family, especially me. I pray that God will bless your organization and the work that you do. I also pray for all of you for everything you did for me during this difficult time." ~ Resident of Phoenix, AZ

SOURCES:

History of Hospice Care. Hospice: A Historical Perspective (2016). Retrieved from:
http://www.nhpco.org/history-hospice-care

National Association for Home Care & Hospice: "Why Hospice is More Important Today Than Ever Before," by Dan Hogan.
http://www.nahc.org/news/why-hospice-is-more-important-today-than-ever-before/

13

FINAL WISHES: THE 7 CS OF GRACEFUL DEPARTURES

By Kevin Haselhorst, MD, emergency room physician, Abrazo Arrowhead Campus, author, "Wishes to Die For."

Margaret, age 82, appeared to be well-cared for by her husband Jim, but was worn out from battling pancreatic cancer for two years. Following the doctor's orders, Jim took Margaret to the ER when she spiked a fever while being treated with chemotherapy.

The ER physician informed Jim that Margaret's white blood cell count was dangerously low and she was at risk of septic shock from an infection. Margaret needed to be admitted to the hospital and started on antibiotics. The physician also informed Jim that Margaret may not have the strength to survive this infection.

Jim gathered his thoughts and with courage declared, "How soon can she be discharged from the ER?" Jim seemed to be following Margaret's instructions and was no longer concerned with the doctor's recommendations. The ER physician asked if Jim had the resources to manage her illness at home, and he replied, "I have the Visiting Angels standing by and ready to help."

While barely saying a word, Margaret seemed to be in total command of the situation. She had prepared Jim for this very moment and he was respecting her final wishes.

Final Wishes Need to Trump Doctor's Orders

The process of aging is like a lifelong journey. You might set goals similar to having an itinerary for a round-the-world cruise. At the end of the cruise, most hope to achieve one goal of everlasting peace. After a long journey, people like Margaret often wish to die in the peaceful setting of their own home. Suffering in the chaotic hospital is rarely on people's list of final wishes. Final wishes should have little to do with following doctor's orders.

The journey of life is filled with breaking points between listening to what others tell you to do and doing what is best for yourself. These breaking points take courage and commitment that inspire personal dignity. Your final wishes need to be geared toward this goal and dying with dignity.

Most people have strong opinions and values about quality of life, but rarely think about their quality of death. It's customary for physicians to treat chronic illness and avoid using the phrase terminal illness. Most patients who do not have a terminal illness are not expected to die and final wishes are neglected as a result. Patients tend to delegate their final wishes to caregivers and healthcare providers who may not be ready to let them go – in their minds "give up" on you. Instead of experiencing a good death, most patients experience a fate worse than death.

Final Wishes Guard Against a Fate Worse Than Death

Patients rarely wish to die until confronted with the consequences of prolonging life, suffering a fate worse than death. A recent study cited these four predicaments:

1. Lacking control over the situation

2. Living in a constant state of confusion

3. Being placed on a breathing machine or requiring a feeding tube

4. Losing control of bladder and bowels

Knowing what you don't want is often easier than determining what you do want. Having an advance directive is a legal document that helps others determine your fate when you can no longer speak for yourself.

But don't mistake your advance directive as being a list of your final wishes. Final wishes take more consideration and need to reflect heartfelt values more than personal desires. Desires often arise when you lack contentment and want more attention. Values allow you to resist temptation and appreciate what you have. Values give you the ability to speak up for yourself with regard to accepting or refusing medical intervention.

Final Wishes Support Advance Directives

Final wishes might imply wanting more or less from the healthcare system. Most people prefer to receive some medical intervention before honoring natural death. But you don't need an advance directive for this.

Advance directives are only relevant if you're incoherent and have a terminal illness. You might be surprised to learn that doctors don't follow advance directives when you can still express your wishes.

Final wishes are best viewed as a work in progress toward a one certain goal – a finish line. Final wishes help prepare you and your family for the end-of-life journey, deeming what life support is necessary to make you most comfortable. Advance directives are most helpful for those who are totally dependent and prefer the right to die naturally. Advance directives are only useful for those who can no longer express their wishes.

The importance of properly completing an advance directive cannot be overstated. If you want peace and comfort at the end, don't make your advance directive a to-do-list. Peace is only achieved through declaring, "I want for nothing."

Follow through with these steps to completing your advance directive:

1. Fill out the proper forms for advance directives offered by the Arizona Secretary of State.

2. Sign the form and make sure your assigned medical power of attorney has a copy.

3. Electronically store and access your document on The Arizona Advance Directive Registry.

4. Review your advance care directive annually or after hospitalization.

5. Provide a copy your advance care directive to your primary care physician.

Final Wishes: Weigh the options of staying alive or resting in peace

Completing and filing advance directives are only the beginning of beginning of advance care planning. Most people wait until the circumstances are dire and have no plan for saying "No" to lifesaving measures. They're often prepared to live as long as possible and ill-prepared to consider the alternative to prolonged suffering – dying in peace. Desperate times call for desperate measures or final wishes.

Desperate Measures

- Full Code Resuscitation
- ICU admission for terminal illness
- Breathing Machine/Feeding Tube
- Futile Surgery
- Dialysis in the elderly
- Experimental Chemotherapy
- Antibiotics for Septic Shock

Final Wishes

- Composure
- Competence
- Commitment
- Certainty
- Conformity

- Compassion
- Comfort

Final Wishes: Sailing the 7 Cs of Graceful Departures

Achieving dignity at the end of life requires advance care planning today. Final destiny awaits for those who have final wishes, yet many people fail to act on their intentions. You rarely get what you want in life without having discipline and overcoming fear.

Final wishes are often geared toward hope rather than following an appropriate sequence. Each step -- composure, competence, commitment, certainty, conformity, compassion and comfort -- requires letting go of anxiety and feelings of failure that sabotage your best intentions.

Sailing the 7 C's is a journey that will take you from being distracted by your fear to having the determination to end life peacefully.

Final wishes cannot be honored by others until you establish what they are for yourself. They're not granted magically and are often discussed in medical terms. The end of life is not a medical conquest; it's a spiritual journey. Physicians and family members are more likely to be afraid of your dying and less likely to honor your final destiny. Each of your final wishes needs to provide the strength for your passage to the afterlife through the concept of "Graceful Departures."

The following seven "C-words" will help you assert your final wishes:

1. Composure

If you wish to be in control, you must maintain composure.

Few of us are prepared to deal with the worst-case scenario or a life-threatening situation. There's a natural tendency to call 911. A 2013 study published in the Journal of the American Medical Association found that most Americans over 65 prefer to die at home but nearly three-quarters die in an institutional setting. The study found an increase in the number of people who do die at home – from 15% in 1989 to 24% in 2007 -- but an increase in the use of the intensive care unit in the last days of life.

When you are diagnosed with end-stage heart disease and begin experiencing symptoms of a heart attack, will you know what to do? Composure allows you to quiet the mind and listen to the heart. The heart provides unconditional love, which might be viewed as the guiding light at the end of the tunnel and a source of strength. Through controlling your emotions, your strength of character and resolve emerge. Composure allows you to regain competence.

2. Competence

You appear competent when making a decision or completing a task. The use of defense mechanisms like denial, anger, bargaining and depression often allows fear to get the best of you.

Will you be ready when the time comes to choose between life support and sedation? Life-and-death decision are often confusing. Yet, if you intend to die in peace, you need the competence to achieve a carefree state by refusing needless medical intervention. Restoring your competence allows you to hold firm to your commitment.

3. Commitment

Integrity in life provides the basis for your commitment.

What was your goal in life? To prolong life to the age of 100 or achieve natural death after the age of 65? Choosing to die sooner than later requires commitment and an advance directive. A survey of 7,900 Americans published in 2014 in the American Journal of Preventive Medicine found that only 26.3% had an advance directive. Therefore, much time is spent on guessing what your goals are rather than honoring your wishes.

With survival in mind, your first thought is to proclaim, "I don't want to die." Your intention for advance care planning might need to clearly express, "I'm willing to die." You declare this pledge in writing by completing your advance directive. This commitment to end unnecessary suffering for you and your survivors provides certainty.

4. Certainty

Final wishes are linked to chronic diseases in that they are something you feel in your bones. Seven out of 10 Americans die from chronic disease such as heart disease and cancer. According to the CDC, 117 million American had one or more chronic diseases as of 2012. Chronic disease leads to terminal disease, which permits final wishes to be granted.

The certainty of death and the desire for dignity supports the adage, *When a door closes another one opens.* When you no longer enjoy quality of life, the door to personal dignity opens. This conviction grants you the wherewithal to rise to the occasion

> Dignity is the certainty of being right.

and go with the flow to life ending. Certainty is easier when there's consensus amongst family members and healthcare providers, all agreeing to one standard for end-of-life care and conformity.

5. Conformity

The ability to accept the things you cannot change allows for conformity.

Most people do not wish to end life without a fight, and rarely know when to cease medical intervention. They often feel like they might appear if they retreat from battle, yet look foolish trying to beat the odds. Almost a third of Americans see 10 or more physicians in the last six months of their lives, according to a CNN poll from 2000. There has got to be a less cumbersome way forward.

Conformity is the blessing inherent to getting everyone on the same page. This generally involves changing the hearts and minds of everyone who is afraid of letting go. When dying is no longer perceived as being wrong, it feel right to end life when the time comes. Dying with dying requires establishing harmony with ourselves, others and nature. Conformity unifies the support for providing compassion.

6. Compassion

Compassion is the permission slip that allows for free choice.

Your focus on advance care planning is best geared toward maintaining control of your medical decisions and receiving compassion. More than 80% of patients with chronic disease say they want to avoid hospitalization and intensive care when they are dying. Home health services that provide palliative care allow you refuse being transported to the ER.

Patients who desire compassion realize that they are not getting better are often reluctant to return to the hospital. But that does not mean they are ready to die. Palliative care provides the compassionate resources for you to be cared for at home without your caregiver feeling negligent. Compassion allows patients to receive their final wishes of comfort.

7. Comfort

At the end of life, the only thing that matters is comfort.

Do physicians and family members need to be trained how to comfort patients? Even when patients have an advance directive, physicians are often unaware of their patients' preferences. A 2014 study published in the Journal of the American Geriatrics Society found that more people have advance directives but that they were largely being ignored.

Taking a personal oath to "do no harm" is a promise that we make to ourselves and provide others. Like the Golden Rule, this needs to be a standard practice of medicine instead of the abuse that is often rendered to the dying. We all want to rest in peace. How we achieve this is through a better understanding how to comfort one another at the end.

Final Wishes Spark Conversations and Bring Peace

There are five conversation you need to have to complete your end-of-life journey:

- Make peace with yourself
- Make peace with your family
- Make peace with your physician
- Make peace with God
- Make peace with hospice

With Yourself

Like any wish, peace must be desired before it is granted. Achieving peace in the end begins with your being ready, willing, and able to surrender. You need to allow nature to take its course if you intend to die with dignity. Having made peace with your final wish for comfort helps family members to end your suffering and respect your passing.

With Your Family

Your family is most likely to struggle with letting go and allowing you to pass. You need to reassure them that it's your choice to have life end and you're at peace with the decision. Selecting the person who will make your final medical decisions when you can no longer speak is a healthcare proxy or medical power of attorney. This person needs to act in your best interest by respecting your final wishes.

With Your Physician

Your physician is often afraid of patients dying and may be the last person to initiate an end-of-life conversation. Physicians feel obliged to present every option for you to stay alive. You owe it yourself to inform the physician that you have final wishes that do not include the "desperate measures" listed previously. Physicians are more likely to provide you hope, you need to remain steadfast in receiving peace of mind.

With Your God

There are two perceptions of God: 1) The One who stands in judgement (requiring redemption and suffering), and 2) The One who offers free choice (allowing for your final wishes without condemnation). The God of free choice offers compassion and peace with your medical decisions. This God is eager to welcome you home through showering you with amazing grace.

With Hospice

Life is a journey deserving of "Graceful Departures." Most people prefer to die peacefully, yet are hesitant to enroll in hospice. Hospice is the safe haven that protects you from that standard practice of medicine that saves lives. If you long to experience a state of peace at the end of life, hospice workers and volunteers will descend upon you like angels of mercy. You simply need to open to them supporting your final wishes.

In Conclusion

We have legal choices about end-of-life care, but we're often at a loss when it comes to letting go of our fear and ending life. Through adopting these final wishes as the way for us all to die with dignity, we might begin to have better end-of-life conversations, reach agreements and provide everlasting peace.

ABOUT THE CONTRIBUTORS

Cynthia Findley: Family Caregiving in Arizona

Cindy Findley, MBA, serves as executive director of the Arizona Caregiver Coalition, which supports and advocates for family caregivers in Arizona under the auspices of the state's division of Aging and Adult Services at the Department of Economic Security. ACC was developed through the Governor's Advisory Council on Aging and serves a mandated role as part of the Arizona Lifespan Respite Program.

Cindy is a Certified Senior Advisor®, a Senior Real Estate Specialist®, Certified Living in Place Professional™ and Certified Readmission Prevention Professional™.

Cindy can be reached at cfindley@azdes.gov.

Learn more about the Arizona Caregiver Coalition at www. AZCaregiver.org.

To reach the Arizona Caregiver Coalition Caregiver Resource Line, call 888-737-7494.

Scott M. Fischer: Assisted Living Communities: How Do You Choose?

Scott, BSN, has dedicated his professional energies to nursing administration, nursing education, home health nursing, and to the care of seniors suffering from dementia. Scott has been a leader in developing and implementing a code of ethics and standards of best practice for the non-regulated senior living referral industry and serves as president and co-founder of the Professional Association of Senior Referral Specialists (PASRS).

Scott also runs Options for Senior Living, which was founded in 2003 to provide professional consultation and guidance service to families and seniors seeking assisted living. He has served over 2,000 families in the past 13 years, many of those who have had a loved one suffer from some form of dementia.

In 2016, Scott joined the Health Care Committee at the Arizona Attorney General's Office. The committee is developing a wide-reaching, comprehensive statewide approach to address the most pressing issues that face Arizona's graying population.

Scott and his wife Stacey have six children between them and one grandson. They live in Queen Creek. Scott loves music and baseball. He grew up in Ohio as a Cincinnati Reds fan and has been an Arizona Diamondbacks season ticket holder since 2002.

To reach Scott, go to scott@optionsfsl.com.

To learn more about the Professional Association of Senior Referral Specialists (PASRS), go to www.pasrs.org.

To learn more about Options for Senior Living, go to www. optionsforseniorliving.com.

Marc Giannone: Minding the Piggy Bank: Planning Your Financial Future

Marc Giannone, Retirement Income Certified Professional (RICP®), guides families through financial planning in all stages of lives. As his clients' personal "CFO," Marc takes a holistic viewpoint, listening carefully to their spoken and unspoken concerns, and helping them create a financial plan that matches their values and goals.

After starting his wealth management career at a large brokerage house, Marc soon came to understand that investors are best served by fee-only, fiduciary advisors -- not stockbrokers. A graduate of Messiah College in Grantham, Pennsylvania, Marc also holds the RICP designation from The American College of Financial Services. He and his wife, Emily, live in Phoenix.

Rhea Go-Coloma: The Hospice Embrace

Rhea Go-Coloma, LMSW, CMFSW, has served as a hospice professional for fourteen years, starting as a patient care volunteer in a skilled nursing setting and working her way up to chief administrative officer of Hospice of the West six years ago.

Rhea, a licensed master social worker with certifications in gerontology and forensic social work, has served the Phoenix community as a caregiver, grant writer, educator, volunteer, social worker and hospice manager.

Rhea, the wife of Frank, a combat veteran and culinary arts instructor, is involved in veteran affairs, leading the We Honor Veterans Campaign at her company. She is working toward her doctorate in organizational leadership.

Rhea has resided in Arizona for 17 years. She was born in the Philippines and raised in Southern California and in Hawaii. Rhea and Frank have two children who keep them busy with soccer, baseball, chess, piano and dance, and two dogs, three turtles and a fish.

You can reach Rhea at rhea.go-coloma@hospicewestaz.com. Learn more at www.hospicewestaz.com.

Kevin Haselhorst, MD: The7 C's of Graceful Departures: Final Wishes

Kevin Haselhorst, MD, practices emergency medicine at Abrazo Health – Arrowhead Campus. He is the author of Wishes To Die For and Sail the 7 C's of Graceful Departures. Kevin's company, Graceful Departures, TM is an expert in advance care planning, and speaks publicly about advance directives, palliative care and ethical standards for end-of-life care.

Kevin earned his medical degree from Southern Illinois University. He is a contributing writer for the Arizona Republic's Ask the Expert Column and a blogger for KevinMD, the Conversation Project, Death café, and wishestodiefor.com.

You can reach Dr. Haselhorst at: DrH@KevinHaselhorst.com
Learn more at KevinHaselhorst.com.

Timothy Holt: Where There's a Will, There's a Way

Timothy Holt is a managing attorney at The Holt Law Group, P.C., in Glendale, which specializes in comprehensive estate planning, including asset protection, tax mitigation planning, and wealth preservation.

Timothy studied chemical engineering at the University of Utah College of Engineering and then earned his law degree at the College of Law, where he served as editor of the Law Review. He has been in practice for 32 years.

You can reach Tim at tim@holttrust.com or by calling 1-623-334-6800

Learn more at www.holttrust.com.

Dana Jean: Managing Your Medications

Dana Jean, MBA, is a Senior Living Advisor with Senior One Source. Senior One Source provides free senior living guidance to families looking for the right care option for themselves or their loved ones.

Learn more at www.senioronesource.net.

Dana's professional background includes community nonprofit work with youth and families. She also works throughout the Valley providing education, workshops, and special events for seniors.

Dana and her husband Chris have two children, daughter Madalyn and son Barrett. She loves being a Girl Scout leader for her daughter's troop.

You can reach Dana at DanaJ@SeniorOneSource.net

Michelle Jewell: The The A,B,C and D (and other basics) of Medicare

Michelle Jewell is a Medicare broker who helps seniors throughout Arizona understand how Medicare works. She is also licensed to sell final expense, health, mortgage protection, annuities and life insurance products.

Before she turned to her current profession, Michelle worked as a real estate agent in Tucson. She is a Raku artist and avid scuba diver who loves to cook and travel – five years ago, Michelle traveled the world solo with a backpack. She recently married her high school sweetheart, Wayne, and they live in Phoenix with their dog, Leroy.

You can reach Michelle at 602-828-9937 or email her at Michelle@ TheInsuranceLadyAz.com

Visit her Facebook page at www.facebook.com/ TheInsuranceLadyAZ

Andy Lockridge: Looking Ahead: The Wisdom of Long-Term Care Insurance

Andy Lockridge, founder of Lockridge and Associates, has been a licensed life and health insurance agent in Arizona since 1995. He teaches courses called "Making Sense of Medicare" and "Making Sense of Social Security" at

various community colleges from Sedona to Tucson. He is also a frequent speaker on Medicare, Social Security, and long-term care for various groups and organizations throughout Arizona.

Andy was the first person in Arizona to receive the National Social Security Advisor certification.

Andy lives in Maricopa with his wife of 43 years, Nancy. They have three children and five grandchildren. Andy has been deeply involved in the community, serving as a youth soccer coach and referee and as a Little League coach. He served as director of the Phoenix FamilyLife Weekend to Remember marriage conferences and as chairman of the Lydia Project, which seeks to raise the standard of living of women in Egypt.

Andy and Nancy serve as part-time staff in their church in the areas of counseling, prayer, and hospital visitation.

You can reach Andy at andy@lockridgeandassociates.com.

Learn more at Andy's websites and Facebook page: https://www.facebook.com/lydiawietsma/videos/857565744375356/

Lockridgeandassociates.com

www.aboutmedicare.org

www.nssconsult.com

Jason May: Long-Term Care: What Will Arizona Cover?

Jason May is an elder law, estate planning and probate attorney who was born in Omaha and grew up in Glendale, Arizona.

Jason got his BA in communications at ASU, where he was a founded member of Young Life ASU West. He graduated from Arizona Summit Law School, where he received several Dean's List awards.

As an attorney, Jason focuses his efforts on helping people achieve their goals and dreams through effective estate planning. As a trial probate attorney, Jason also helps clients find and close loopholes in their plans. As a counselor at law, Jason helps advocate for his clients' goals and wishes while maneuvering complicated family dynamics efficiently and peacefully.

Jason teaches Sunday school at his church. His hobbies include traveling, antiquing and gardening. He and his wife Holly have a dog and a cat.

You can reach Jason at 480-360-0537 or at Jason@gaudiosilaw.com

Learn more at www.gaudiosilaw.com

Edward Perrin, MD: Finding the Right Doctor for You

Edward Perrin, MD, is medical director of Iora Primary Care in Glendale.

As a family physician and geriatrician, Ed enjoys working as a part of a team taking care of the whole patient in the context of their families and communities.

Ed served as president of the Arizona Geriatrics Society and has been recognized as a "Top Doc" in Geriatrics in Phoenix Magazine.

His educational history includes an undergraduate degree from Harvard College and his medical degree from the University of California at San Diego School of Medicine in La Jolla.

Ed's free time is devoted to his wife and three children, and their pet menagerie that consists of two dogs, three cats, two turtles, and one tortoise.

You can reach Dr. Perrin at Edward.perrin@ioraprimarycare. com.

To learn more about Iora Primary Care, go to www. ioraprimarycare.com/phoenix or call 602-833-7422.

Mindy Wakefield: Navigating the Care of a Person with Dementia: Strategies

Mindy Wakefield, MSW, serves as strategic collaboration manager at the Alzheimer's Association Desert Southwest Chapter in Phoenix, supporting programs and services for dementia patients and training family caregivers. She also provides education to professionals, first responders, and various community organizations.

Mindy's professional experience includes non-profit program and business management, medical social work, government social services, counseling and case management.

To reach Mindy, go to mindy.wakefield@alz.org

Learn more about the Desert Southwest Chapter at www.alz. org/dsw/ or by calling 480-297-2361.

ABOUT THE AUTHORS

Presley Reader, MPA, is the co-host of "Aging in Arizona," a 3-year-old weekly radio show on 960 AM The Patriot that features interviews with community and business leaders about aging-related issues and services. Presley also owns and operates a ComForCare Homecare franchise in the West/Northwest Valley of the Sun. ComForCare provides in-home caregiving services in Glendale, Peoria, the Sun Cities and Surprise. For more information, visit www.comforcare.com.

Presley volunteers as a speaker for the Alzheimer's Association, and has worked in the nonprofit world, in business and in government. Most importantly, he has been married for 14 years and has three children.

Mark Young, MPA, is Presley's co-host and president of ComForcare Home Care in the East Valley. His office has been rated as one of the top 4% in the country for all home care agencies for the last 6 years by Home Care Pulse, a distinction based on client and caregiver's reviews.

Mark has worked with the Alzheimer's Association for more than 5 years as an educator and caregiver support group facilitator. Mark is a past president of Arizona In-Home Care Association (AZNHA).

Go to www.comforcare.com for more information about us.

Steve Alfonsi: MA

Steve's father owned skilled nursing and rehabilitation facilities in multiple states, exposing Steve to the senior assistance industry from an early age. When his mother was faced with a pancreatic cancer diagnosis, he learned firsthand what it takes to be an effective and loving caregiver.

Today, Steve, MA, is owner and operator of ComForCare Home Care, which serves Scottsdale, Phoenix, Paradise Valley, Anthem, Cave Creek, Carefree, Rio Verde, Fountain Hills and surrounding areas. His company provides in-home assistance with Activities of Daily Living such as bathing, dressing, medication reminders, transportation, and more.

Steve has a certification in ComForCare's DementiaWise program and national certification as a hospital readmissions professional.

Steve has a master's degree in economics. He is a sponsor of and a frequent guest on "Aging in Arizona," a radio show on The Patriot (AM 960) that is hosted by ComForCare franchisees Presley Reader and Mark Young.

Steve and his wife Nancy (co-owner of ComForCare) have two children, Cole and Morgan. Steve loves outdoor activities, including mountain biking and skiing.

Steve can be reached at steve@cfcaz.net.

Learn more about ComForCare at www.scottsdaleaz.comforcare. com or www.ComForCare.com.

Resources

Caregiving

Arizona Caregiver Coalition:
Ph. 1-888-737-7494
Website: Azcaregiver.org

The Arizona Caregiver Coalition administers the Arizona
Respite Rebate Program, which allows family caregivers
to be reimbursed for respite services they procure and are
available to family caregivers on a quarterly basis. Call the
ACC for eligibility information.
The Arizona Respite Locator:
Ph. 1-888-737-7494
Website: https://www.rewardingwork.org/

Alzheimer's Association – Caregiving:
Website: www.alz.org/care

Arizona Long Term Care System (ALTCS) (provides
in-place care services for individuals meeting Medicaid
guidelines):
Ph. 1-800-654-8713
Website: http://www.azahcccs.gov/applicants/application/
ALTCS.aspx

Housing

Options for Senior Living (assists families and
seniors seeking assisted living options): www.
optionsforseniorliving.com
LeadingAge Arizona (provides an online director of more
than100 residential facilities including assisted living
facilities, senior housing, retirement communities and
nursing homes):
Ph.1-602-230-0026
Website: http://leadingageaz.org/

Insurance

Medicare:
Ph. 1-800-633-4227
Website: www.medicare.gov

State Health Insurance Assistance Program (SHIP) (provides
assistance to Arizonans with Medicare questions):
Ph. 1-800-432-4040
Website: https://des.az.gov/services/aging-and-adult/
state-health-insurance/arizona-state-health-insurance-
assistance-program-1

Medicaid (Arizona Health Care Cost Containment System):
Ph. 1-602-417-6600
Website: https://www.azahcccs.gov/members/
ALTCSlocations.html

Alzheimer's disease and other Dementias

Alzheimer's Association
Ph. 1-800-272-3900
www.alz.org

To find your local chapter of the Alzheimer's Association:
www.alz.org/crf

Palliative and Hospice Care:

Hospice Directory (to locate a hospice near you)
Ph. 1-800-854-3402
Website: http://www.hospicedirectory.org/cm/search

Hospice of the Valley
Ph. (602) 530-6900
Website: https://www.hov.org/

Arizona Hospice and Palliative Care Organization
Ph. 1-480-491-0540
Website: http://www.arizonahospice.org/

National Hospice and Palliative Care Organization (provides resources and a local hospice locator):
Ph. 1-800-646-6460

https://moments.nhpco.org/find-a-hospice

General

Area Agency on Aging Region One (Maricopa):
Ph. 1-888-783-7500
Website: http://aaaphx.org/

Arizona Area Agencies on Aging (Arizona Division of
Aging and Adult Services):
Ph. 1-602-542-4446
Website: azaging.org

Arizona Healthy Aging (part of Arizona Department of
Health Services):
Ph. 1-602-542-1025
Website: http://www.azdhs.gov/prevention/tobacco-
chronic-disease/healthy-aging/index.php

Eldercare Locator (connects to services for seniors by state):
Ph. 1-800-677-1116
Website: www.eldercare.gov

Arizona Association of Providers for People with
Disabilities:
Ph. 1-602-510-9373
https://www.caregiver.org/arizona-association-providers-
people-disabilities-aappd

Arizona Adult Protective Services (APS) and Elder Abuse
Hotline:

Ph. 1-877-767-2385 (877-SOS-ADULT)

For hearing impaired: 1-877-815-8390

Website: https://des.az.gov/services/aging-and-adult/arizona-adult-protective-services-aps

Arizona Technology Access Program (provides resources for assistive technology devices, services and funding):

Ph. 1-800-477-9921

For hearing impaired: 1-602-728-9536

Website: http://www2.nau.edu/aztap-p/